# The Old Royal Observatory Greenwich

# *The Old* Royal Observatory Greenwich

## Guide to the Collections

National Maritime Museum

Merrell Holberton
Publishers London

ISBN 1 85894 069 9

First published in 1998 by
Merrell Holberton Publishers
Willcox House
42 Southwark Street
London SE1 1UN
in association with the
National Maritime Museum

Designed by Stephen Coates
Produced by Merrell Holberton Publishers

Printed and bound in Italy



Front cover top: Flamsteed House, 1675-76, the original building of the Observatory; John Arnold's pocket timekeeper no. 36, 1778
bottom: Chart of the North Atlantic by Mount and Page, 1702; Armillary sphere by Antonio Costa, 1676
Back cover: The Time Ball on Flamsteed House
Frontispiece: The Old Royal Observatory from the north

At the end of each caption the object's inventory number is given; also, in square brackets, its photographic negative number.

# CONTENTS

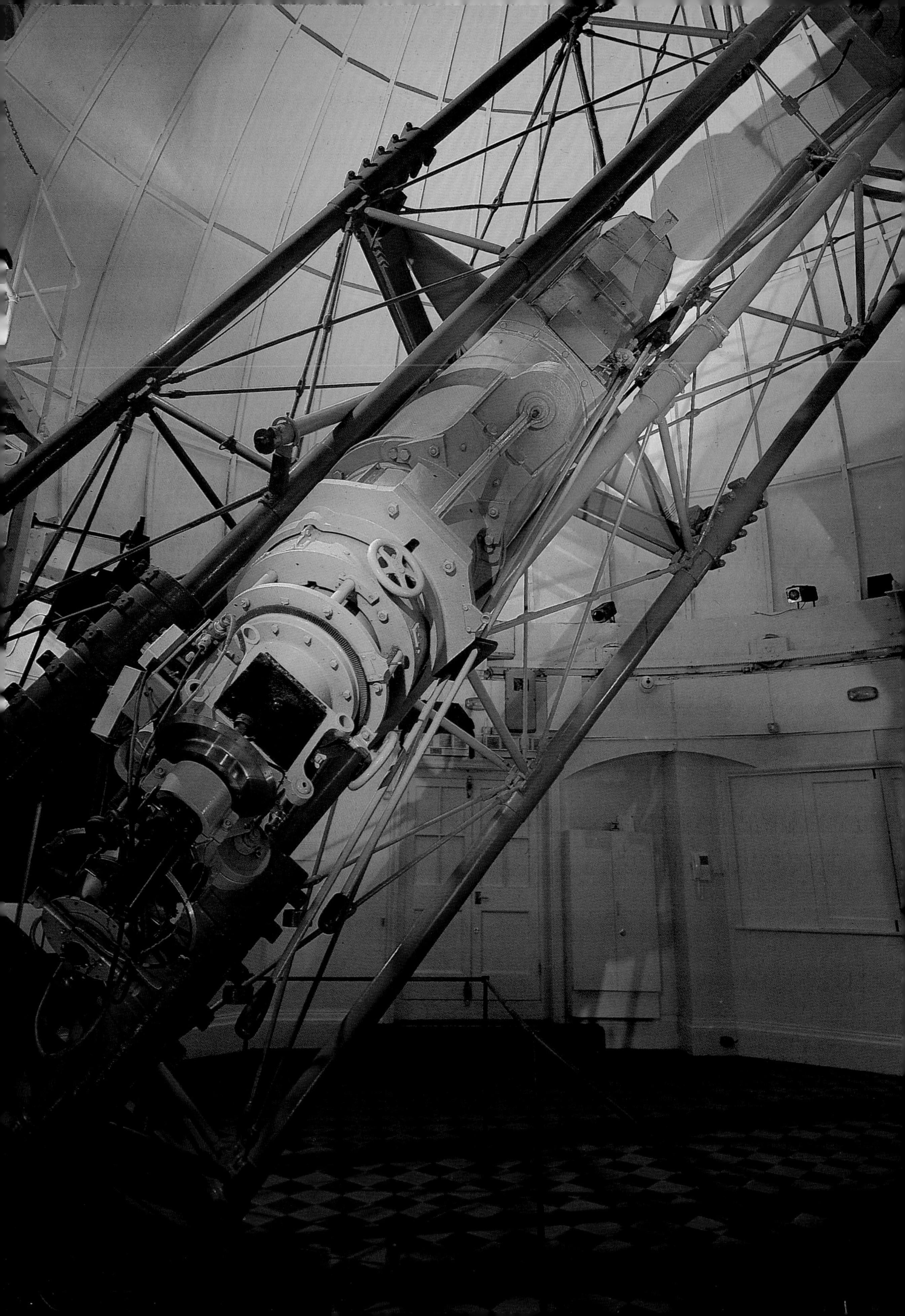

# THE ROYAL OBSERVATORY

## *Centre of Time and Space*

For over 300 years the Royal Observatory has overlooked the River Thames at Greenwich, where it was established in 1675 by King Charles II 'in order to the finding out of the longitude of places for perfecting navigation and astronomy'. At a time when safer navigation was critical to Britain in its rivalry with other European powers for seaborne wealth and expanding colonial possessions, the first Astronomer Royal, John Flamsteed, launched a programme of mapping the stars, making the first step towards developing the 'lunar distance method' of finding longitude at sea.

Almost a hundred years later the longitude problem was finally solved through both astronomy and the development of the marine chronometer. It was at this point that the Royal Observatory began its more general involvement with developing 'Greenwich time'. By the mid nineteenth century the Observatory was working on the establishment of public time-keeping standards, supplying time via railway telegraph lines to the rest of the country. Since the International Meridian Conference held in Washington DC in 1884, the principal transit circle at Greenwich has been used to define the Prime Meridian of Longitude and hence the time-zone system for the whole world.

Light pollution eventually forced the Greenwich astronomers to look for clearer skies and, when they moved to Sussex in the 1950s, the Observatory became part of the National Maritime Museum. The buildings offer displays which explain the history of time- and space-measurement and the Observatory's link with the story of navigation. There are over seven thousand scientific and horological instruments in the Museum, and while limited space allows only a fraction of these to be displayed, all are accessible on advance request to those who are interested. This guide introduces some of the highlights of the collections particularly connected with the Royal Observatory and its work.

**The Greenwich 28-inch Great Equatorial Refracting Telescope of 1894** (See pages 92 and 95)

# CHAPTER ONE

# THE STARS AND THE SEA

## *The Astronomy Collection at Greenwich*

**Astrolabe, Persian, 1659–60**
The astrolabe is a mathematical model of the heavens. Its name in Greek means 'star-taker'. Although its origins are buried in ancient history, it is a remarkably sophisticated scientific instrument. It is one of the earliest forms of computer, used to solve astronomical problems and to show the positions of stars and planets at different times, dates and latitudes. This beautiful gilt-brass example was made by the prominent maker Muhammad Mahdī. Among the fine engraving, in Persian calligraphy, is a poem in praise of the astrolabe and a quotation from the Koran, 'The world is decorated with the stars'.
*AST0594 [B9024-C]*

The National Maritime Museum's collections of instruments of astronomy, navigation, hydrography and precision timekeeping, associated with its best known site, the historic buildings of the Royal Observatory in Greenwich Park, are unrivalled in the world.

Safe ocean voyaging has always depended on the art of navigation: the use of charts, of instruments to observe the Sun, Moon and stars; and of chronometers, by which the navigator transforms time measurements into positions on the featureless ocean. In all this, the information provided by astronomers is crucial. Hence the close links which exist between practical seafaring and astronomy, and their equal importance in the collections of the Museum and the role of Greenwich in Britain's maritime history.

Navigation was not always accurate or easy. When the Observatory was founded by Royal Warrant of King Charles II in 1675, it was specifically in order to solve the greatest scientific puzzle of the age – 'the longitude problem', or how to find the east-west position at sea necessary to give an accurate 'fix' when combined with the more simply found north-south co-ordinate of latitude. It was believed that accurate maps of the night sky could help solve the problem and to make other navigational improvements. In 1675, the King, a great

**Sundial by David Asselinne of Dieppe, about 1610**
Many scientific instruments are also fine works of art, full of interesting detail. This ivory and silver dial is engraved with a view of Dieppe surrounded by scenes of ships and dolphins. The decoration is continued on the outer case with a storm-driven ship, monsters and foliage. Set alongside these are the mathematical scales and dials used for telling the time, including a lunar volvelle which shows the phases of the Moon. Through science and art, this object makes the crucial link between navigation and time-keeping. Working in ivory and bone is a craft for which Dieppe, on the Normandy coast, was long famous.
*AST0177 [D8842-D]*

Of meridians, and parallels,
man hath weaved out a net,
and this net thrown upon the heavens,
and now they are his own.
JOHN DONNE (1572–1631)

patron of science, appointed John Flamsteed to compile these celestial charts. The first Astronomer Royal at Greenwich, Flamsteed held the post to his death in 1719. By then, the oldest part of the buildings was already known as Flamsteed House, as it still is.

For the first 175 years of its existence, the work of the Observatory was almost exclusively related to the needs of navigation. The successive Astronomers Royal were charged with meticulously measuring the relative positions of the stars and Moon, creating functional and beautiful celestial charts. It took almost 100 years for the longitude problem to be solved by astronomical means when, in 1766, the first edition of *The Nautical Almanac* was published under Nevil Maskelyne, who was fifth Astronomer Royal from 1765 to 1811. Just a few years before this, the perfected 'chronometer' of clockmaker John Harrison had been tested at Greenwich, and at sea, as a more practical method for most seafarers to use.

When Sir George Biddell Airy, the seventh Astronomer Royal, entered the Observatory in 1835, it had long been famous but its work was highly specialized around positional astronomy. Airy made sure that it became a great national establishment, consulted for advice on a wide range of scientific subjects. He gradually replaced all the instruments by new ones of his own design and introduced a programme of regular magnetic, meteorological and solar observations. Under Airy, Greenwich Mean Time – based on the Prime Meridian of Longitude which he established here in 1851 – was distributed to the rest of the country through the railway telegraph network. It was adopted as legal time in Great Britain in 1880 and in 1884, by agreement of the International Meridian Conference in Washington DC, it became the basis of the entire world time system.

At the end of the nineteenth century, developments in photography and spectroscopy also gave rise to

**Urania's Mirror, constellation cards, published by Samuel Leigh about 1825**
Under the blanket of night, stars appear like a jumble of pin-pricks of light. From the most ancient times, civilizations have given names and mythologies to conspicuous patterns of bright stars to help make the sky seem more familiar. This charming set of 32 hand-coloured constellation cards was developed in the early 19th century as an educational tool. Each tissue-backed card depicts a major constellation with pierced holes corresponding to the size and magnitudes of the brightest stars. Held up to the light they give a realistic representation of the constellation patterns, guiding the novice astronomer around the night sky.
*AST0049 [D9281-4]*

**Nocturnal by Amerigo Leone of Rome, 1589**

A nocturnal is used to find the time at night, making use of the fact that the stars in the northern hemisphere appear to circle anti-clockwise around the Pole Star, completing one revolution in just under 24 hours. The position of the stars can thus be read like the hour hand on a clock. The index arm of the nocturnal is aligned with Ursa Major or Ursa Minor, the constellations of the Great Bear and Little Bear, so that it indicates the time on a numbered scale. In the dark, the hour can be discovered by feeling and counting the little teeth cut into the scale. The instrument is so simple that sailors themselves often made nocturnals out of wood. This silver example is quite elaborate and can be used for predicting other astronomical phenomena, such as the phases of the Moon.

*AST0130 [D8925]*

**Hour-glass, English, about 1630**
The hour- or sand-glass is designed to measure intervals of time according to the flow of fine particles. The name is a little misleading since these glasses typically measure any period from a few seconds up to several hours, and may be filled with any granulated substance: sand, ground marble, eggshell or even ground human remains! For many centuries they were used on board ship to mark the timing of the watches and, with a log line, for calculating speed and distance run. This one times one hour: holes in the base plate are for threading the ropes used to hang the glass from a beam, isolating it from the motion of the ship.
*AST0080 [B3772]*

Stand still you ever-moving spheres of heaven,
That time may cease and
midnight never come ...

CHRISTOPHER MARLOWE (1564–1593), *DR FAUSTUS*

**William Herschel's 7-foot reflecting telescope, 1770–90**
Using a telescope similar to this, Herschel made his famous discovery of the planet Uranus in 1781. It was the first planet to be identified since antiquity, although John Flamsteed had observed it in 1690 thinking it was a star. Herschel wanted to call it 'The Georgian Planet', after King George III, but Roman mythology prevailed: Uranus was the father of Saturn and grandfather of Jupiter, names already given to other planets. The discovery brought Herschel to the attention of the King, who granted him a pension of £200 a year, which he supplemented by the sale of telescopes made to this design.
*AST0960 [D7107]*

**Planisphere by George Philip & Son, about 1935**
The modern descendant of the astrolabe, the planisphere (literally 'flat sphere') compresses an entire hemisphere of stars into a small, hand-held map. It is adjustable to show the positions of the stars above your head for any date and time, and demonstrates how the constellations cartwheel around the Pole Star, bobbing above then below the horizon throughout the year. Modern planispheres are made from functional plastic but this early 20th-century example is made from card with elaborate gilt decoration. They are made for a specific latitude: this one is for 51½° North, suitable for London and Leipzig.
*AST0595 [D4437-C]*

the new science of astrophysics. Sir William Christie, eighth Astronomer Royal (1881–1910), set about modernizations at Greenwich to meet the demands of the new discipline. Christie expanded the Observatory in terms of staff, expertise and buildings. He oversaw construction of the New Physical Observatory, now known as the South Building. He helped launch the Observatory into the twentieth century by installing the 28-inch Great Equatorial refracting telescope housed in its now familiar onion-dome. This telescope, although now over 100 years old, remains the largest refractor in Great Britain and the eighth largest in the world. It is in full working order, recently upgraded with the addition of a computer system to speed up the process of locating particular stars and planets.

Today, the public galleries of the Observatory display the succession of observational *(cont. p. 16)*

**Celestial globe by Gemma Frisius of Louvain, 1537**

The National Maritime Museum holds one of the most comprehensive collections of globes in the world. This is the oldest, one of a unique surviving pair, of which the terrestrial example is in Vienna, designed by the physician and mathematician Gemma Frisius and made in the Louvain workshop of Gaspard van der Heyden. Its engraving is the earliest known work of Heyden's pupil, the great cartographer Gerard Mercator. It shows the northern stars in their familiar mythological constellations, but with large gaps in the southern hemisphere, still largely unknown to Europeans in the 16th century. Navigators used celestial globes to compare with their own astronomical observations, though Frisius was probably more concerned with astrological purposes. Made of paper, plaster and wood, globes tend to be extremely fragile and sensitive to light and heat. For this reason, the Museum collection spends much of its time in an environmentally controlled store.
*GLB0135 [D7958-B]*

**The South Building, built 1894–99; photographed in about 1910**
Originally called the New Physical Observatory, this building was largely designed by the eighth Astronomer Royal, William Christie, working with the architect William Crisp. Each of its four wings housed a different branch of the Observatory: magnetic and meteorological work in the north wing, astro-photography in the west, time in the south and the library in the east. The outside is decorated with Doulton terracotta, including the names of 24 eminent astronomers and scientific instrument makers, an Art Deco carving of the Muse *Astronomia* and with a bust of John Flamsteed, the first Astronomer Royal, over the entrance. The dome originally accommodated a 30-inch (76 cm) reflecting telescope by Henry Thompson, visible in this photograph. In 1908, the eighth satellite of Jupiter was discovered using this telescope. In the 1950s, this splendid late-Victorian addition to the Observatory was considered worthless and there was a serious proposal to demolish it, fortunately not carried out. *[P39986]*

**A Dollond refracting telescope, late 18th century**
At less than 6 inches (15 cm) high, this is the smallest telescope in the Greenwich collection. Even so, its eye-piece has a rotating wheel of four differing lens powers. When John Dollond and his son Peter started an optical instrument company in the early 18th century, astronomical observations suffered because of the poor quality of glass available for telescope lenses. John Dollond worked with higher-quality glass to produce a lens free from chromatic aberration (distortion of an image with fringes of coloured light). Within ten years, every observatory in Europe had upgraded its telescopes with this achromatic lens. The Dollond name is still familiar in Britain as part of a chain of opticians.
*AST0933 [D2018]*

> You never enjoy the world aright,
> till the sea itself floweth in your veins,
> till you are clothed with the heavens,
> and crowned with the stars.
>
> THOMAS TRAHERNE (1637/39–1674)

instruments used by the Astronomers Royal, almost since Flamsteed's time. But probably the most important 'object' in the astronomy collection is the site itself, the complex of buildings on the hill in the middle of Greenwich Park. These were transferred to the care of the National Maritime Museum (NMM) during the 1950s, when the astronomers forsook the polluted skies of London for the clearer views of Herstmonceux in Sussex and, later, the Canary Isles. The research body became known as the Royal Greenwich Observatory, while the original buildings in Greenwich passed to the NMM.

The Duke of Edinburgh, a Trustee of the National Maritime Museum, opened the Observatory's Octagon Room to the public in May 1953 and HM The Queen opened the whole of Flamsteed House in July 1960. November 1965 saw the inauguration of the Caird Planetarium in the South Building and in 1967 the restored Meridian Building was opened. In May 1975, the Queen commemorated the 300th anniversary of the Observatory's foundation by recommissioning the 28-inch telescope, newly returned from Herstmonceux, in the reconstructed onion-dome.

The Astronomy collection today comprises the telescopes which have an historical association with the Royal Observatory, as well as significant collections of astrolabes, sundials, globes, planetaria and other relevant instruments. By far the largest proportion of objects were donated by Sir James Caird (1864–1954), a Scottish ship-owner and the Museum's greatest benefactor. From the 1920s until his death, Caird generously supported the purchase of collections and individual objects for the NMM (which was officially opened by King George VI in April 1937) acting on the advice of the Museum's first director, Sir Geoffrey Callender (1875–1946). Their acquisitions of *(Cont. p. 24)*

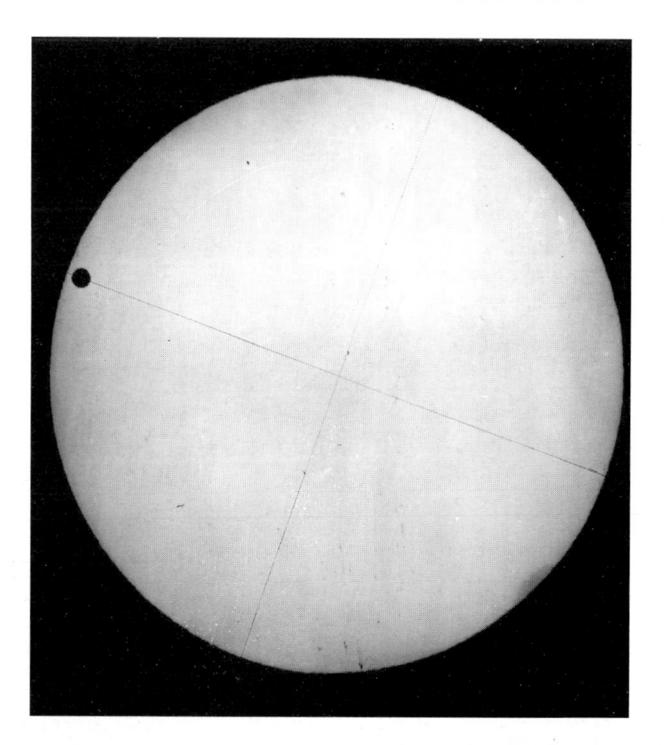

**Glass negative of the Transit of Venus, 1874**
Astronomical records improved enormously with the advent of photography. This example, taken at Luxor in Egypt, shows the planet Venus as a small dot silhouetted against the large disc of the Sun. Every 113 years or so, Venus passes directly between the Earth and the Sun. In 1716, Edmond Halley, later the second Astronomer Royal, predicted that our distance from the Sun could be calculated from simultaneous observations of this phenomenon taken from different points on the Earth. These transits happen in pairs but Halley died before those of 1761 and 1769 proved his theory true. It was to observe the 1769 transit that Captain James Cook was first sent to the South Seas. The next pair will occur in 2004 and 2012.
*AST1085 [B5948-H]*

**The Altazimuth Pavilion, built 1899**
The Altazimuth Pavilion is named after the special telescope originally installed in its dome. This instrument was designed to measure the two co-ordinates used to fix the position of a celestial body – the altitude (position above the horizon corresponding to terrestrial longitude) and the azimuth (position east along the horizon). The instrument no longer survives and the dome now contains another type of telescope called a photoheliograph, used to observe the Sun by projecting an image of the solar disc on to a flat plate. The weather vane over the dome represents Halley's Comet as shown in the Bayeux Tapestry. This picture also shows the open 28-inch telescope dome.
*[D3161-9]*

**Signet ring with horizontal sundial, Swiss, 16th century**
The last word in pre-mechanical portable time-keeping, this fashionable Renaissance finger ring has a lid which flips up to reveal a horizontal sundial with a tiny compass for orientation. The crest and initials on the front may be used with sealing wax as a signet. The earliest sundials were often a simple stick in the ground; the shadow they cast as the Sun moved across the sky indicated the time of day. Later, more accurate dials were erected on church walls and in town squares for public use. Smaller ones were made for the pocket and anybody who could afford an early watch or clock would also own a sundial to check its accuracy.
*AST0531 [C4723–19]*

**Sunshine recorder by John Francis Campbell, 1876**
Meteorological conditions, such as changes in atmospheric pressure and temperature, can affect astronomical readings. James Bradley (third Astronomer Royal, 1742–62) started regular barometer and thermometer readings in 1750, a practice which continued unbroken until 1956 and remains the longest series of readings in the United Kingdom. On being appointed, George Airy (seventh Astronomer Royal, 1835–81) established a Magnetic and Meteorological Department with James Glaisher as Superintendent. This sunshine recorder was one of the instruments used. It works on a simple principle. The Sun's rays are focussed through a glass sphere, and the burning point traces a smoky line on a strip of card, indicating the hours during which the Sun has shone.
*AST0770 (bowl) and AST769 (sphere) [D9251]*

**Magnetic dip circle by Troughton & Sims, 1860**

During the 19th century, the Observatory became an important centre for measuring changes in terrestrial magnetism – vital to compass navigation. This instrument was designed by George Airy to measure the 'dip' or vertical component of the Earth's magnetic field, in much the same way as a compass measures the horizontal component. Magnetic instruments are extremely sensitive and those at Greenwich were badly affected by the electric railways introduced after the First World War. A new site free from artificial disturbances was found near Abinger, in Surrey, but with railway electrification there after the Second World War the site had to be moved again, this time to Devon.
*AST0701 [D9241-2]*

**Terrestrial globe by Vincenzo Maria Coronelli of Venice, 1688**
At over 3 feet (1 metre) in diameter, this is the largest globe in the collection. Coronelli (1650–1718) was a Franciscan friar who became celebrated for making large-scale globes. In 1684, he established the first geographical society, of which members paid subscriptions to receive the gores (printed globe segments) which he published in Venice and which could be assembled on locally made spheres across Europe. This globe was assembled in Vienna in 1752–54 under the supervision of another mathematical friar, Tobias Eder, then well over 80 years old. It is littered with explanatory notes and historical facts, many incorrect, and Coronelli has even included his own portrait.
*GLB0123 [D7690-N]*

**Armillary sphere by Antonio Costa of Ferrara, 1676**
One of the earliest astronomical instruments, the armillary sphere is primarily a dynamic model of the universe demonstrating the motions of the heavens as observed from the Earth. It is named from the Latin word for 'ring' after the hoops which make up its skeleton. The overall shape is based on the Ptolemaic concept of the universe as a sphere, with Earth at the centre, an idea established in antiquity. Each ring represents a different celestial coordinate with the ecliptic, or path of the Sun, running just inside the tilted silvered zodiac band.
*AST0620 [D7936-A]*

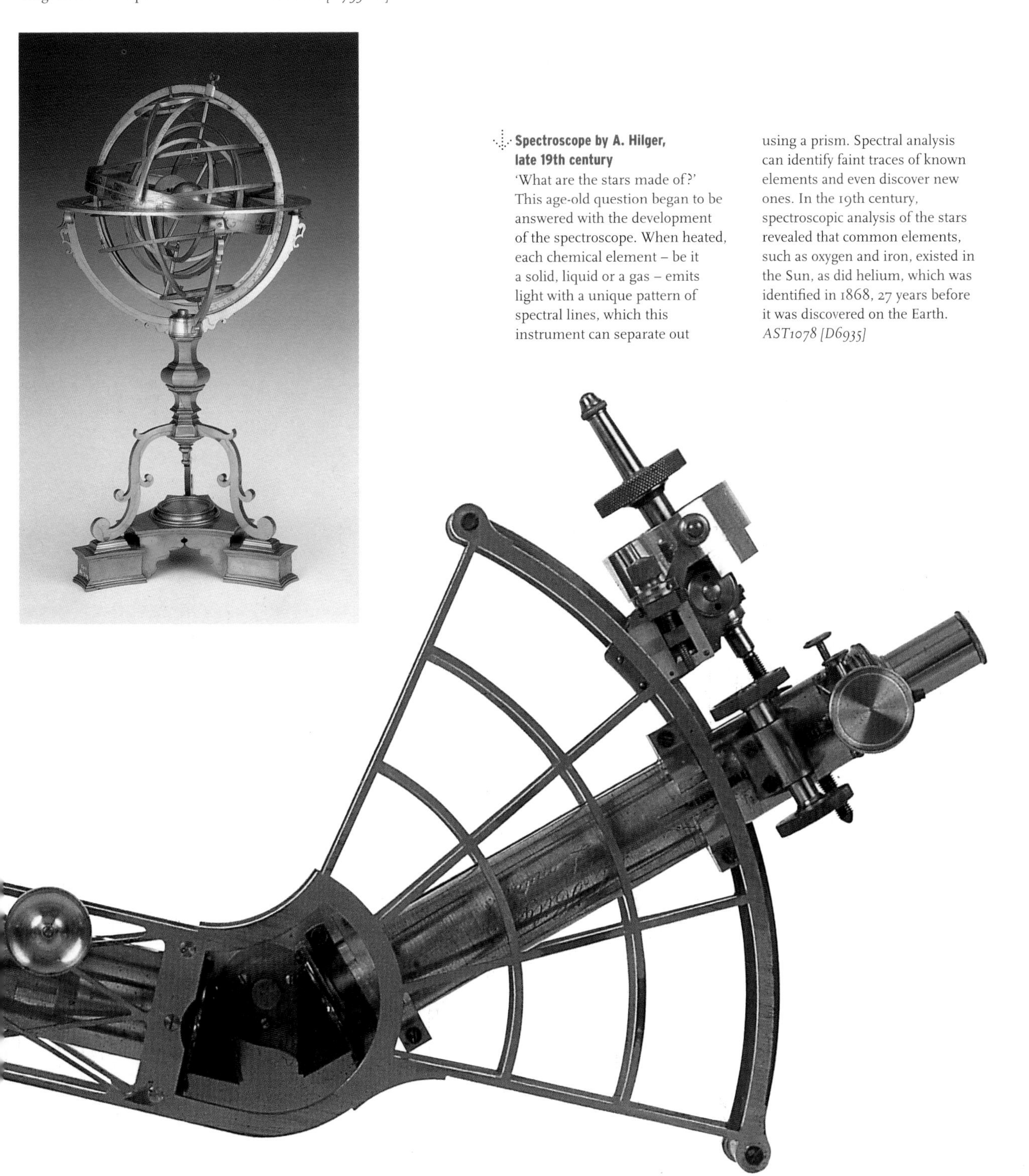

**Spectroscope by A. Hilger, late 19th century**
'What are the stars made of?' This age-old question began to be answered with the development of the spectroscope. When heated, each chemical element – be it a solid, liquid or a gas – emits light with a unique pattern of spectral lines, which this instrument can separate out using a prism. Spectral analysis can identify faint traces of known elements and even discover new ones. In the 19th century, spectroscopic analysis of the stars revealed that common elements, such as oxygen and iron, existed in the Sun, as did helium, which was identified in 1868, 27 years before it was discovered on the Earth.
*AST1078 [D6935]*

**Planetarium by William and Samuel Jones, 1794**
A planetarium is a mechanical model of the solar system which may be operated by hand or clockwork. This example has a carefully engraved base-board giving astronomical information. Among other things, it shows tiny images of the planet Saturn and the position of its rings as observed from the Earth in different years. Interestingly, given its date, it has not been corrected to include William Herschel's discoveries of the planet Uranus in 1781 and two new satellites of Saturn in 1789.
*AST1062 [A2367-B]*

**Astronomical game published by John Wallis, 1804**
During the 18th and 19th centuries, as people became fascinated by the wonders of science, demonstrations and lectures on scientific subjects became increasingly popular. Educational toys were introduced to make learning fun, and among the educational tools in the Observatory collections is this board game – *Science in Sport, or the Pleasures of Astronomy*. Using counters, the players progress 35 steps, acquiring knowledge about the heavens on the way. The winner is the first to arrive at Flamsteed House in the centre of the board.
*AST1151 [D6585–23]*

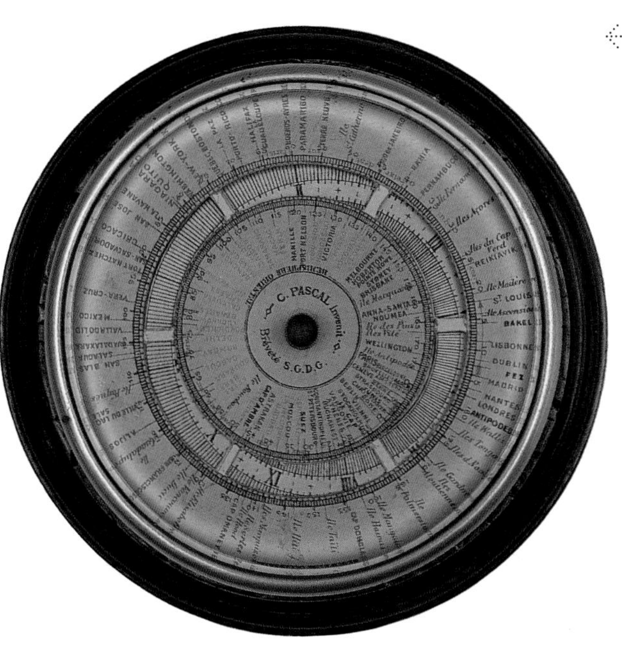


**Universal time-finder by Cesare Pascal, late 19th century**

Time surrounds us in the form of wrist-watches, public and domestic clocks and the timers in common electrical equipment such as video recorders: we tend to take it for granted. The time we now use to regulate our lives in Britain is the same across the country and has been since 1880 when Greenwich Mean Time became the national standard, even though in astronomical terms there is over twenty minutes' difference between the longitude of Greenwich and that of Land's End. With improved communication and transport in the 19th century, people other than astronomers and navigators became aware of time differences within and between countries. This time-finder indicates local time differences in cities around the world in relation to Paris.
*AST0700 [D9240]*

**Astrolabe, English or French, early 20th century**

The date engraved on this instrument is 1659 but stylistic errors show it is a modern fake. Art forgeries have been a problem for centuries, but those of scientific instruments are a relatively recent development – the result of their becoming collectable. Fakes, however, should not be dismissed as the clever fake often betrays a great deal of information about the assumptions of its maker. The engraving on this astrolabe is of very high quality and it should be admired as an excellent piece of metalwork in its own right.
*AST0553 [D9239-2]*

But I am constant as the northern star,
Of whose true-fix'd and resting quality
There is no fellow in the firmament.
The skies are painted with unnumber'd sparks,
They are all fire and every one doth shine ....

WILLIAM SHAKESPEARE (1564–1616), *JULIUS CAESAR*

navigational and astronomical instruments – no less than in all other areas of the Museum's collections – form the basis of the scientific treasures connected with the Observatory. It has been estimated that, by the time of his death, Caird had donated over £1.25 million to the Museum, probably worth over a hundred times as much today.

There are several other major collections of instruments and charts at Greenwich which deserve mention. These include the Herschel Collection of instruments and equipment belonging to that famous astronomical family; the Gabb Collection of scientific instruments; John Harrison's celebrated marine chronometers; and the collection of charts and instruments belonging to the hydrographic surveyor, Admiral John Lort Stokes. Many smaller collections and individual instruments also have fascinating origins, and all contribute to the most comprehensive concentration of maritime artefacts in the world.
*Maria Blyzinsky, Curator of Astronomy*

**Celestial globe, Islamic, undated**
Traditional Western globes are usually of the Earth (terrestrial), the heavens (celestial), or occasionally of the Moon (lunar). Some modern examples show Mars, Venus or other planets. The Islamic world seems only to have produced celestial globes. This metal globe is engraved with 48 constellations and has 67 stars of inlaid silver. Arabic and Persian astronomy was based on that of the ancient Greeks and Romans. The great star tables compiled by the astronomer Ptolemy are the original source for most of the constellations shown here. *GLB0007 [D8042]*

**Navicula sundial, European, 15th century**

The oldest sundial in the collection, this is a medieval example called a *navicula de Venetiis* or 'little ship of Venice' because that is what it resembled. It is an exceptionally rare instrument and only five are known today. No bigger than the palm of a hand, it is used to tell the time by measuring the altitude of the Sun through a pair of sighting holes and noting the altitude off a plumb line. When made accurately, most dials can indicate solar time to within about fifteen minutes. This one is calibrated for five English cities: Exeter, London, Oxford, Northampton and York. It had been buried for over five centuries when found in 1989. The fine condition of the engraving suggests it was almost new when lost.
*AST1146 [D8339-A]*

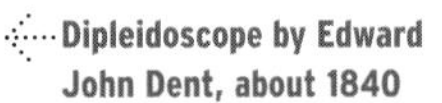

**Dipleidoscope by Edward John Dent, about 1840**

A cross between a sundial and a transit instrument, the dipleidoscope provides an accurate time-check for local noon, when the Sun passes directly over the meridian of the observer. It consists of two prisms, each with two silvered sides which act as mirrors. The eye sees two images of the Sun, one in each prism, moving towards each other as the Sun appears to travel across the sky. At precisely noon, the two images converge into one. The dipleidoscope disappeared from the market shortly after 1852, when the electric telegraph became the common means for time-distribution across the country.
*AST0183 [D8931]*

**Clockwork celestial globe by Isaac Habrecht of Strasbourg, about 1646**
Although a late-Renaissance piece and relatively 'old-fashioned' for its date, this fine and complex clockwork globe is of very high quality. The globe itself revolves at sidereal rate and, by lining up a compass (now missing) on the top, could be used to relate the heavens directly to the stars shown on the globe. This picture shows the clockwork mechanism, with the outer globe removed.
*GLB0174 [D8013E]*

# CHAPTER TWO

# IN STEP WITH TIME

## *The Clocks and Precision Timekeepers*

If there is one place which, wherever they live, people think of when the subject of timekeeping is mentioned, it has to be the Royal Observatory at Greenwich. For more than 300 years the Observatory has played a central role in matters concerning horology – the study of timekeeping and time-telling. The Prime Meridian, running through the Airy transit telescope at the Observatory, was chosen by international agreement in 1884 to define Longitude 0° for the world. In agreeing to this, the world recognized Greenwich Mean Time (GMT; known, in its modern form, as Universal Co-ordinated Time or UTC) as the international time scale.

From the foundation of the Observatory, the Astronomer Royal has needed accurate clocks, known as regulators, to make the star charts with which the great longitude problem was to be solved. For modern astronomers, the two co-ordinates used to fix the position of a star are 'declination' (the height above or below the horizon) and 'right ascension' (the star's angle around the horizon, similar to longitude on Earth), which is the time at which the star appears to cross the meridian of the observer. Thus, to establish the exact right ascension of a star, a very accurate clock set to star time (or sidereal time) is needed. Sidereal time runs slightly faster (3 minutes 56 seconds per day) than solar time (Mean Time) and separate clocks are needed to show the two time-scales.

At the time the Observatory was founded, Europe, and England in particular, were experiencing a

**Astronomical table clock, signed by Caspar Buschmann of Augsburg, about 1586**
The Renaissance was the period when Germany produced its finest and most interesting clockwork; this is a typical and splendid example. The clock is said to have belonged to Casimir V, King of Poland, who took it to Paris when he abdicated and became Abbot of St Germain. He died in 1672. The clock has an astrolabic dial and strikes the hours and the quarters. Additional dials provide information on the lunar cycle and the calendar, including the dominical letter for each day of the year and indicators for the old style Julian calendar and the new style Gregorian calendar. Despite being signed by Buschmann, the complex mechanism was almost certainly made by Johann Reinhold.
*ZAA0011 [D9245]*

Dost thou love life?
Then do not squander time,
for that's the stuff life is made of.

BENJAMIN FRANKLIN, *POOR RICHARD'S ALMANACK*, JUNE 1746

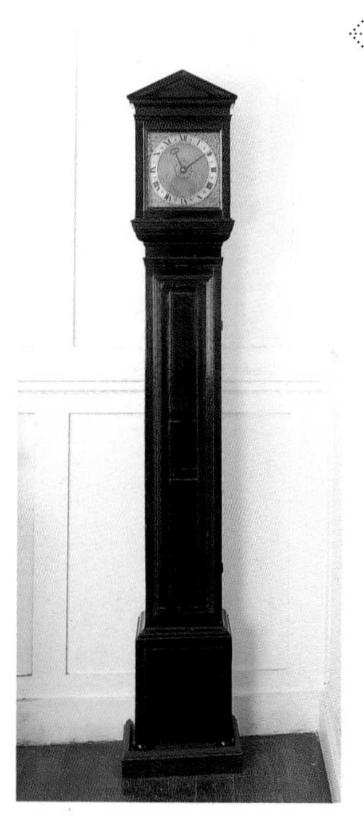

**Pendulum longcase clock by John Fromanteel of London, about 1665**
Ahasuerus Fromanteel and his son John were the first to make pendulum clocks in England after their invention in Holland. With the new pendulum as controller, clocks were capable of time-keeping to within a few seconds a day, as opposed to about half an hour a day with earlier designs. The earliest were simple wall clocks, but because they ran for eight days and had heavy weights – they tended to fall off weak plaster walls! The longcase clock was introduced in about 1660 for better support.
*ZAA0260 [D9259]*

scientific 'Golden Age'. Very much part of this exciting and productive period in England was the work of the London clockmakers – so it was also the horological Golden Age. Over the years, almost every one of the 'state-of-the-art' designs for precision clocks was made in London and for use at Greenwich in the world's leading observatory. Many of these unique regulators are still on display in the same buildings, and the horological collection – about 1000 pieces in all – is generally recognized as the finest of its kind.

By a fitting, if somewhat ironic turn of events, the longitude problem was eventually solved by a clockmaker just before the astronomers at Greenwich completed their solution (the lunar distance method). It was a Yorkshireman, John Harrison, who in 1759 created the first practical marine chronometer, his

**Three-month-going astronomical longcase clock by Edward Cockey of Warminster, about 1710**
A copy of a clock made for Queen Anne in 1705, this is one of four almost identical known clocks of this type by Cockey. The 24-hour dial has an hour hand represented by a sun motif which is loosely intended to follow the real Sun in the sky. At sunset the sun disc disappears behind a shutter, reappearing from behind another shutter at dawn. The shutters are controlled by the clock mechanism and move up and down during the year to ensure 'sunrise' and 'sunset' occur at the correct time. In the centre of the dial is an annual calendar and the moon phase indication.
*ZAA0598 [D4945-4]*

**Year-going pendulum clock by Thomas Tompion, London, one of a pair made for the Observatory in 1676**
These clocks were originally built into the panelling of the Octagon Room and had 13-foot (396 cm) pendulums suspended above them. They were removed in 1719 by the widow of the first Astronomer Royal, John Flamsteed, and sold as domestic longcase clocks. One is preserved at the British Museum and the other has now returned to Greenwich. This picture shows a detail of the movement. The prime achievement of these two clocks was to prove that the Earth spins on its axis at a uniform rate.
*ZAA0885 [D8930]*

**Harrison's first marine timekeeper, 'H1'**
John Harrison (1693–1776) made his first experimental marine timekeeper in Barrow-on-Humber between 1730 and 1735, as a first step towards solving the longitude problem and winning the great £20,000 prize offered by the British Government. Now known as 'H1', the timekeeper is unaffected by the motion of a ship owing to its two interconnected swinging balances. It compensates for changes in temperature and, thanks to extensive anti-friction devices, runs without any lubrication. It was the first relatively successful marine timekeeper of any kind and was the toast of London when Harrison unveiled it in 1735. It is one of the great milestones in clockmaking history.
*ZAA0034 [D6783-A]*

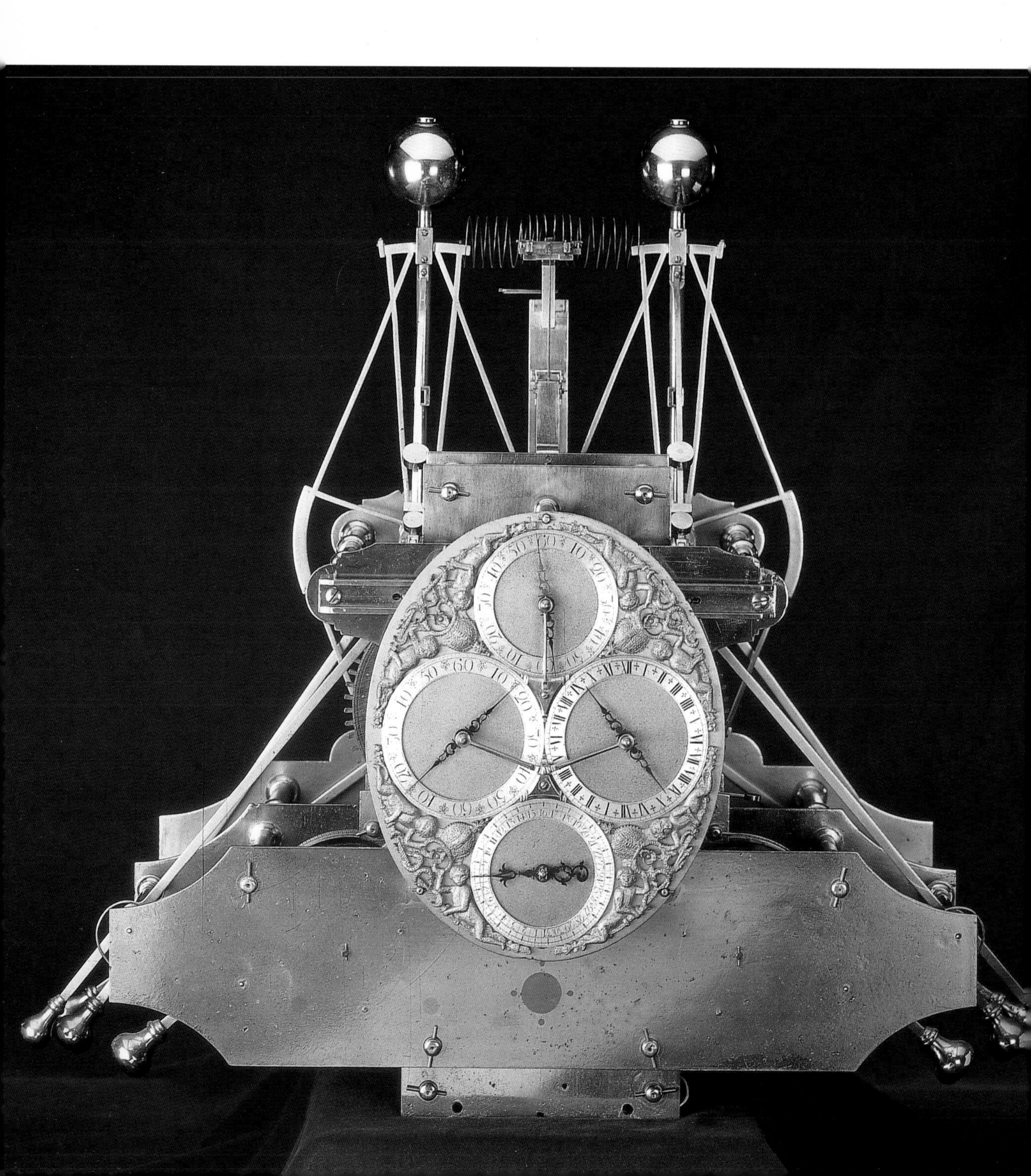

> I have b[r]ought a clock to go nearer the truth than can be well imagine'd, considering ye vast number of seconds of time there is in a month, in which space of time it does not vary above one second ....
>
> JOHN HARRISON, 1730

fourth timekeeper, 'H4', which was also the first of all precision watches. The four great Harrison timekeepers form the 'jewels in the crown' of the 250 marine chronometers and precision watches, of all types and dates, preserved in the National Maritime Museum.

The astronomical work at Greenwich continued after the invention of the chronometer. However, the testing of new, more effective and less expensive designs for marine chronometers also became very much part of the role at the Observatory throughout the nineteenth century. This also involved the purchase and distribution of chronometers to the Royal Navy's ships, and a system was set up which was to everyone's advantage. Makers would send their best chronometers for trial at Greenwich, assured of a ready sale, while the Observatory was able to cream off Britain's best instruments exclusively for Admiralty use. The Museum is fortunate to hold the extensive manuscript records of the Observatory's issue of chronometers to the Royal Navy. This now forms the basis of the International Chronometer Index, in which the Museum is recording data on all known chronometers in this country and abroad. About 50,000 *(cont. p. 37)*

**'H2', John Harrison's second timekeeper**
Made between 1737 and 1739, this is a larger and more solidly built version of H1, with the additional refinement of a remontoire – a device to ensure that the drive to the two balances is as uniform as possible. It is probable that Harrison, who had moved to London by this time, had some help in making parts of H2. Because he discovered a design fault with its balances, Harrison never allowed H2 to be tested at sea. He kept it running at his house for many years until, in 1766, it was taken from him by the Astronomer Royal under the conditions of the longitude prize.
*ZAA0035 [D6784-B]*

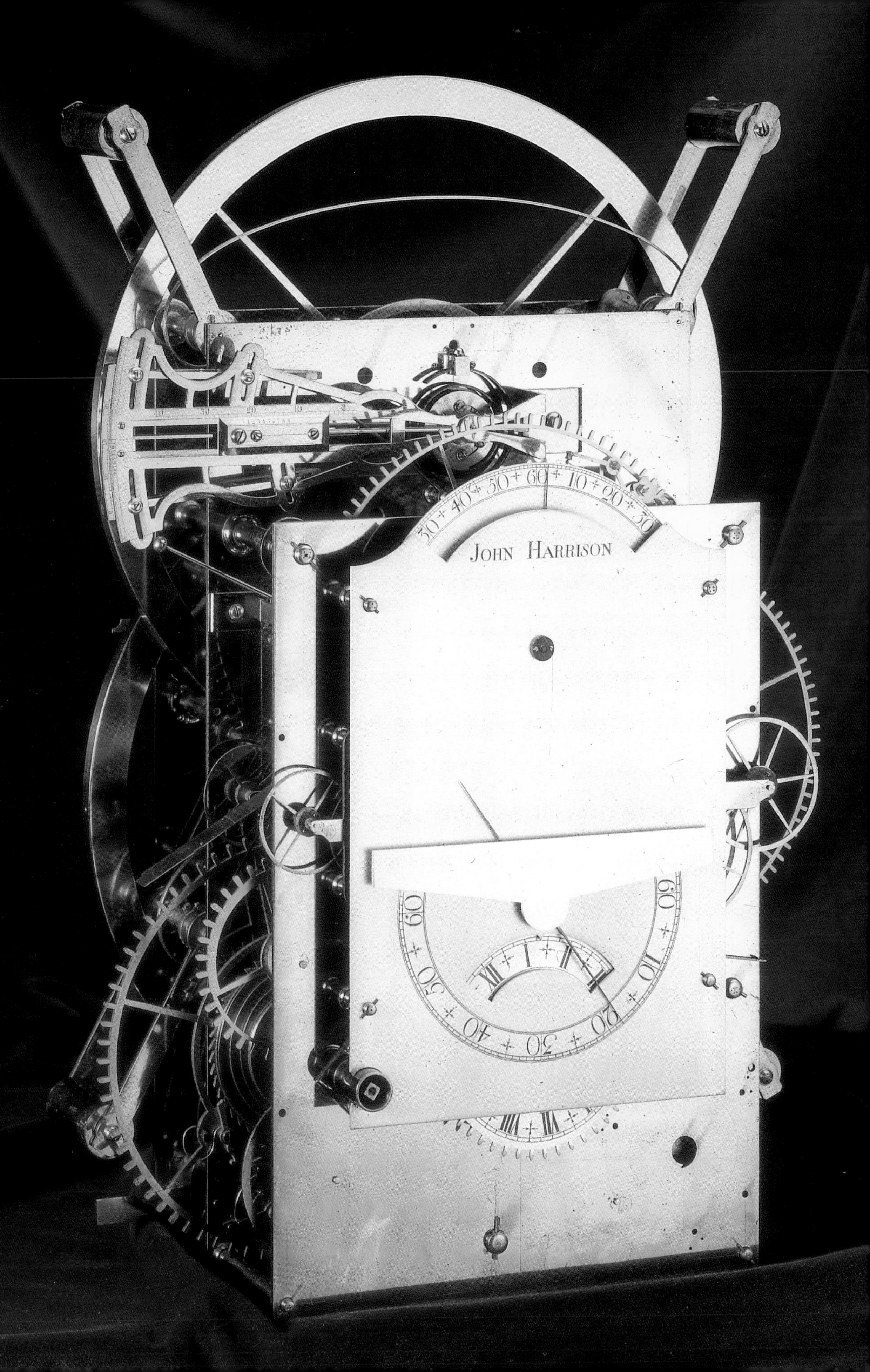
JOHN HARRISON

**John Harrison's third timekeeper, 'H3'**
Started in 1740, H3 took Harrison nearly nineteen years to build and adjust, although it was not to win him the great longitude prize: he found that he just could not persuade the two large, heavy, circular balances to keep time well enough. Nevertheless, H3 incorporates two extremely important inventions, both relevant today: the bimetallic strip (still in use worldwide in thermostats of all kinds) and the caged roller bearing, a device found in nearly all modern mechanical engineering.
*ZAA0036 [D6785-C]*

**Harrison's prize-winning longitude watch, 'H4', completed in 1759**
Harrison had been working on improving watches as a sideline to his development of the much larger H3. In 1753 a pocket watch was made to Harrison's design by watchmaker John Jefferys. This went so well that Harrison began to realise that it pointed to the longitude solution – not in H3 but in smaller watches. Work began on H4 in 1755 and, with its very stable, high frequency balance, it proved the successful design. It is shown here at almost actual size.
*ZAA0037 [D789-A]*

**Cook's chronometer, 'K1', the first copy of H4, made in 1769 by Larcum Kendall of London**
Commissioned by the government from Kendall in 1769, K1 was issued to Captain James Cook on his second and third voyages of discovery to the South Seas in 1772–75 and 1776–80 in order to test its effectiveness. At first Cook was a little sceptical, but the watch behaved so well he learned to trust it, referring to it in his log as his '... never failing guide ...'. It was thus K1 which proved to a doubting scientific establishment that H4's success was no fluke.
*ZAA0038 [A5512]*

**The 'Bounty' watch, 'K2'; made in 1771 by Larcum Kendall of London**
K1 cost £500 and this simplified version cost £200. But while Kendall was a first-rate watchmaker, he was not a good designer and K2 did not keep time very well. It is chiefly famous because it was with William Bligh on the *Bounty* in 1789 when, after the mutiny, it was taken by Fletcher Christian to Pitcairn Island. In 1808 it was bought on Pitcairn from the last survivor of the mutiny and returned to England in 1840.
*ZAA0078 [A5510]*

... if the watchmakers do not know
what o'clock it is,
they can know by going to Greenwich for it ...

THOMAS WRIGHT, CLOCKMAKER, 1783

**'K3', Kendall's third marine timekeeper**
Made in 1774, K3 was an even simpler version of K1, costing just £100. It joined Captain Cook on his third, ill-fated, voyage to the Pacific, from which he did not return. Like K2, the watch did not perform as well as K1, based on Harrison's original. After this final failed attempt to simplify Harrison's design, Kendall began to follow the work of John Arnold.
*ZAA0111 [B1589]*

**The first 'chronometer', by John Arnold of London**
John Arnold (1736–1799) successfully found the way to simplify Harrison's timekeeper design. This watch, No. 1/36, made in 1778, went so well on trial at Greenwich that Arnold decided to give it a new name. In the pamphlet he published in 1780 advertising his achievement, he called the timekeeper a 'chronometer' and was thus the person who invented the term in its modern sense. The watch is in fact a pocket chronometer and is in a 22-carat gold case.
*ZAA0129 [D8566]*

**Marine chronometer by Thomas Earnshaw of London, about 1800**
Following the work of John Arnold, the London watchmaker Thomas Earnshaw (1749–1829) further simplified the designs of the pocket and marine chronometer into their modern, readily reproducible form. This is a typical example of Earnshaw's marine chronometer, made from the early 1790s until his retirement in about 1810. Basically the design is very little different from the marine chronometer of the mid 20th century.
*ZAA0006 [D8744]*

**Silver pocket watch by Thomas Leyden of London, No. 1305, about 1793**
The watch is engraved *Watch worn by Capt. Thomas Masterman Hardy at Trafalgar 1805*. Although it is a relatively ordinary pocket watch of the day, and there is no corroborating evidence, there is no reason to doubt that this watch belonged to Captain Hardy of the *Victory* and was present in 1805 when Horatio Nelson was killed at the Battle of Trafalgar. *JEW0231 [D9247]*

entries are already in place and much information is available to answer enquiries about specific instruments.

With technological advances in the early nineteenth century came another new role for the Observatory, that of time distribution to the public. In 1833 the famous Time Ball was installed on the eastern turret of Flamsteed House in order to provide Greenwich Mean Time for ships in the rivers and docks below, enabling them to set their marine chronometers. However, as the railways and the electric telegraph system began to expand in Britain, ordinary people found they needed a source of GMT too. The public was experiencing increasing problems and confusion using local times across the country; the local time difference between Dover and Penzance (about 300 miles apart, east to west) is nearly 30 minutes and people communicating instantaneously by electric telegraph at a specified time would need to agree whose time. A single time for the nation was the logical answer and the Greenwich Observatory was the obvious provider. In 1852 the Astronomer Royal, George Biddell Airy, bought one of the first new electric master-and-slave clock systems by London clock and chronometer maker Charles Shepherd. A single pendulum clock with electrical

**Remains of a pocket chronometer retrieved from the Franklin expedition to the Arctic in 1845**
This is pocket chronometer No. 980 by Parkinson & Frodsham, about 1810, which was issued to Sir John Franklin's expedition on 10 May 1845 for use on board the *Erebus*. The expedition was to discover whether or not there was a North-West Passage to the Pacific round northern Canada. It disappeared with no survivors; most apparently froze to death. The watch was recovered by Captain F.L. McClintock from an abandoned boat on King William Island. *AAA2203 [D9246]*

**The Flamsteed House Time Ball**
With increasing numbers of ships carrying marine chronometers and needing to set their instruments to GMT, the Observatory installed the first Time Ball in 1833, signalling 1 pm every day to enable the master to set his chronometer before leaving the docks on the Isle of Dogs opposite Greenwich. At 12.55 pm, the Ball rises halfway up the mast. At 12.58, it climbs to the top, and at 1 pm it drops; the instant it begins to move signals the precise time. The Ball is dropped at 1 pm and not 12 because the astronomers are too busy observing the Sun transiting the meridian at noon and setting their clocks. The present Ball dates to 1919.
*ZAA0277 [D5600]*

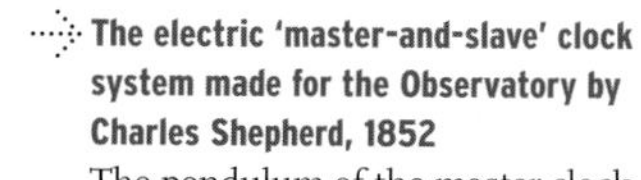

**The electric 'master-and-slave' clock system made for the Observatory by Charles Shepherd, 1852**
The pendulum of the master clock, centre, closes electrical contacts at every swing and controls any number of local 'slave' dials, like those on either side, using electrical pulses. Hourly or daily signals were sent out further afield using the railways' electric telegraph system, to enable clocks all over Britain to be set correctly. After 1852, the Greenwich Time Ball was also released automatically by this master clock.
*ZAA0531 [D9280]*

**The Shepherd gate clock, 1852**
The 24-hour electric slave dial was made by Charles Shepherd as part of the system supplied to Greenwich in 1852. This was the first clock dial to provide Greenwich Mean Time to the public. The minute and second hands are conventional but the hour hand goes round the dial once in 24 hours. Thus, at midday the minute hand points to the top, but the hour hand points to the bottom. Shepherd describes himself as 'patentee', but he had a long-running battle with Scottish clockmaker Alexander Bain, who claimed a prior patent for such an electric clock.
*ZAA0533 [D5601]*

contacts (the master) controlled an almost infinite number of 'slave' clock dials and indicators. Initially the system was confined to controlling small dials, the large gate clock (also by Shepherd) and the Time Ball at the Observatory. Within the year, however, it was extended, using the telegraph lines on the railways to provide GMT to London, then to south-east England, and ultimately the whole country. GMT signals were even sent to the USA once the transatlantic cable was laid in 1866.

In 1924 the Royal Observatory refined its time distribution service by providing the six-pip time signal every quarter of an hour to the BBC, who have broadcast it ever since (usually only on the hour). One of the first clocks to perform this duty was the Shortt 'free pendulum' clock No. 16 of 1927, still at the Observatory today. The precision timekeeping collections come right up to date, and a Hewlett Packard caesium atomic clock and examples of radio-controlled watches and clocks, correct to *(cont. p. 43)*

SHEPHERD,
PATENTEE
London
GALVANO - MAGNETIC - CLOCK
SHEPHERD PATENTEE
LONDON
SHEPHERD PATENTEE
CALVANO MAGNETIC CLOCK

**A ship's clock (bulkhead clock) by the Chelsea Clock Co. of Boston USA, about 1910**
The clock strikes the ship's watches, from one to eight bells, every half an hour. Twelve is eight bells, half past twelve is one bell, one o'clock is two bells and so on, until four o'clock, which is eight bells again. The two, shorter, 'dog watches' (not struck by this particular clock) are between 4 pm and 8 pm, during which the bells struck are 1, 2, 3, 4/ 1, 2, 3, 8. The purpose of the dog watches was to create an odd number of watches, ensuring crews would have changing watches each day and would occasionally have a shorter shift to serve.
*ZAA0107 [D9248]*

**Novelty clock with a figure of a sailor at the helm**
The sailor rocks from side to side in time with the pendulum. Made in France from about 1885, these clocks were in fashion throughout the late 1880s and 1890s. They were part of a series of novelty clocks, all in patinated bronze and brass cases and featuring industrial and maritime subjects. Others included a locomotive with revolving wheels, a steam hammer with oscillating hammer and a submarine with revolving propeller. They featured in the Paris Exposition of 1889 and again in 1900.
*AAA3640 [D9244]*

**Precision regulator by Dent of London, No. 1906, 1870**
This clock was the sidereal standard regulator at the Observatory from 1870 until it was superseded in 1920. It has a highly sophisticated 'detached' detent escapement designed by the Astronomer Royal, Sir George Airy, himself. The pendulum is compensated for temperature and for barometric pressure changes, and is also one of the first of its type. The present glass-fronted case was a replacement made for the clock when it was exhibited at the 1951 'Festival of Britain'.
*ZAA0601 [D9279]*

Time and space are fragments of the infinite,
for the use of finite creatures.

HENRI FRÉDÉRIC AMIEL, *JOURNAL*, 16 NOVEMBER 1864

**Gold pocket watch retrieved from a victim of the Titanic disaster, 1912**
A 27-year old Scot, Robert Douglas Norman, was a passenger on the *Titanic* when she sank on 15 April 1912. This watch, which would have been reset daily to the ship's time, must have stopped almost immediately he was in the water, at 3.07 in the morning. One of the search parties recovered his body several days later, with the watch still in his pocket.
*ZBA0004 [D8137]*

'Time goes' you say; Ah no, alas!
Time stays, *we* go.

ANON.

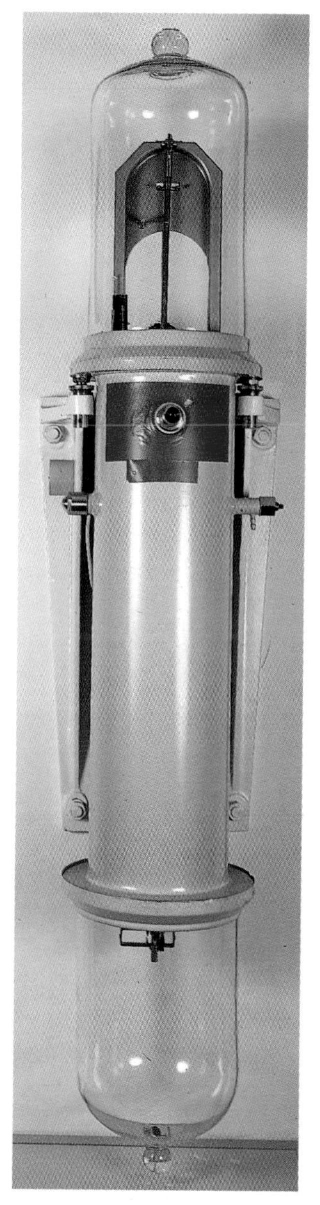

**The ultimate pendulum clock, Russian, 1970**
This high-precision pendulum clock, designed by Feodosii M. Fedchenko of Moscow, is said to be the most accurate design ever created. The pendulum swings to electronic impulses in an almost total vacuum. About fifty of these clocks, which have a normal electric dial (not shown here), were made for use in television centres, railway termini and airports throughout the former Soviet Union. They had the advantage over the more accurate quartz and atomic clocks that they were easy to set up and were robust and reliable – essential qualities in the more inhospitable and remote corners of the USSR.
*ZAA0760 [D8913]*

**High precision 'free pendulum' clock by W. H. Shortt, London, No. 3, 1927**
The 'master' pendulum of the clock swings in a partial vacuum within the glass-topped cylinder (left) and is given impulses to keep it swinging by a secondary pendulum in the middle. The Shortt system was capable of keeping time to within about a second in a year. The cylinder on the right holds the pendulum from Shortt No. 16, which was the clock used for controlling the BBC 'six pips' and the Post Office time signal from 1927 to 1935.
*ZAA0594 [D5608]*

**Radio-controlled wristwatch by Junghans of Germany, 1990**
The watch receives a digital radio time signal from Frankfurt which ensures that, within a range of about 1000 miles, it is always correct to within a small fraction of a second. The aerial is built into the leather strap. Subsequent models have analogue dials (*i.e.* with hands) and have the aerial in the ceramic case with a solar panel to provide energy for the movement.
*ZAA0741 [D6937]*

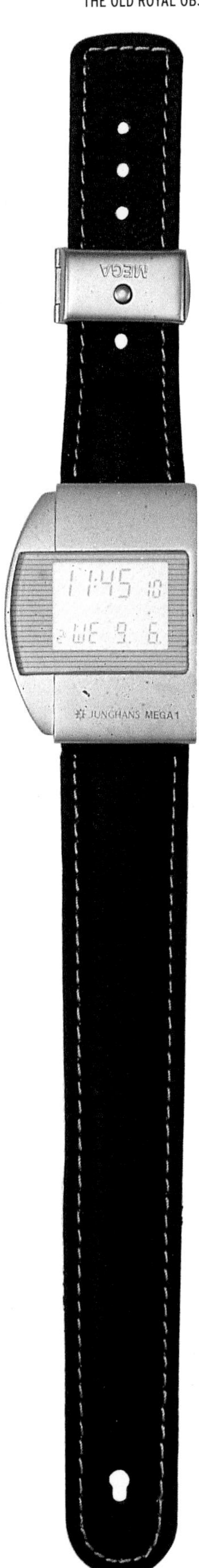


within a few thousandths of a second, represent up-to-the-minute technology.

The Observatory is, of course, part of the National Maritime Museum, and the horology collection includes objects of more specifically seafaring interest too. Apart from the obvious ship's bells clocks, there are clocks and watches commemorating great naval campaigns, timepieces once the property of important naval figures and even relics from famous expeditions and maritime disasters such as the sinking of the *Titanic*. Other objects have complex astronomical indications, including some fine Renaissance clocks and mechanical globes. On the lighter side, amusing novelty clocks show that clockmakers were not always the dull and technical souls we might imagine. The Robert Foulkes bequest of 1986 brought the NMM many high-quality domestic clocks and watches from all periods, which, in spite of having no maritime or astronomical association, round off this unique collection perfectly, ensuring it is not just of interest to scholars of the history of science but to all who enjoy fine antique clocks.
*Jonathan Betts, Curator of Horology*

**Replica of the Congreve rolling-ball clock, 1972**
Instead of a pendulum or a balance to keep time, a small ball-bearing rolls down a zig-zag track on a tilting tray. Once the ball has rolled to one end, which takes 15 seconds, it triggers the mechanism to tip the tray up the other way and off it goes again. The original clock, patented by William Congreve in 1808, was intended as a high-precision timekeeper. Congreve must have been very disappointed as it cannot keep time to better than within about 20 minutes a day!
*ZAA0176 [D9177]*

# CHAPTER THREE

# TOOLS OF THE MARINER

## *The Navigational Instruments*

In ancient and medieval times, the most important element in navigation was the judgement and experience of the mariner. Only a few adventurous peoples set off on voyages across vast expanses of ocean to land in territories previously unknown to them. The majority of traders relied on well established routes, never far from land, and the ability to recognize coastlines and landmarks. Many journeys required only experience, good observation, and a lead and line for sounding the depth of the water. Charts, rutters (or *routiers*, route directions) and pilot books provided a way of passing on knowledge of different coastlines to new generations of seamen. Much important trade, especially in spices and silk from Asia, relied primarily on overland routes, with only the final stage across the land-locked Mediterranean Sea by ship. Long-distance oceanic voyages were much more hazardous, and, before the fifteenth century, were undertaken, for the most part, only by the Arabs, the Polynesians and the Vikings. These peoples appear to have relied on

**Compass, probably Italian, about 1570**
The earliest compass in the Museum's collection is made of turned ivory and dates from the second half of the 16th century. The inner bowl with the compass card is mounted in a brass gimbal ring to reduce the effects of the ship's motion at sea. The soft iron needle is diamond-shaped and is fixed to the underside of the vellum and paper card, which is divided into 32 points. The north and east points have additional decoration, a feature which remained common up to the 19th century, east for most Europeans being the direction of the Holy Land. Most early compasses had wooden bowls, so this example, made of expensive ivory, must have been intended for a person of wealth.
*NAV0276 [A1763]*

**Compass by William Farmer, about 1750**

Compass design changed little between the 16th and mid 18th centuries. Compass cards were hand-painted and often very decorative. This one has symbolic figures of the planets Jupiter, Mars, Mercury, Venus and Saturn, together with the Sun and Moon. It is graduated in degrees as well as compass points. The turned wooden bowl has been painted green and the needle is of soft iron, which had to be re-magnetized every so often with a piece of magnetite, or lodestone. The compass is inscribed *Made by William Farmer near the Limekiln Horsley Down*. This was in Bermondsey, on the south bank of the River Thames, opposite the Tower of London and close to the busiest part of the port.
*NAV0227 [D5213]*

**Compass by George Adams, 1766**

Inscribed *Made by G. Adams, Fleet Street, London. Instrument maker to His Majesty, 1766.* The first major improvement to the mariner's compass came in the mid 18th century with the work of Dr Gowin Knight. In 1745 he invented a method of making strongly magnetic steel bars, and then developed a steel compass needle which retained its magnetism for much longer than the old soft iron kind. George Adams, the London instrument maker, was employed as agent for Knight's compasses and this example has the signature Gowin Knight 1180 on the back of the card. It was part of the Admiralty Compass Observatory Collection, which was transferred to the National Maritime Museum in 1969.

*NAV0447 [B8566]*

a knowledge of the trade winds and observations of the Sun and stars to find their way. The Arabs used the trade winds to sail between the east coast of Africa and India.

During the Middle Ages the invention of the magnetic compass provided an extremely useful navigational aid for voyaging out of sight of land. Its great advantage was that it enabled the mariner to know in which direction he was sailing, even when the sky was obscured by cloud and he could not see the Sun or stars. The first reference to the compass in Europe was in a late twelfth-century treatise by Alexander Neckam. It was known earlier in China, but so far no evidence has been found to show conclusively whether the Europeans learnt of the compass from the Chinese or invented it independently.

During the fifteenth century, Western Europeans became increasingly interested in finding a sea route to Asia, after the break-up of the Mogul Empire disrupted the peaceful overland trade in silk and spices. Exploration, and the subsequent establishment by European powers of colonies in the Americas, Asia and Africa, acted as incentives to find better methods of navigation. Both commercial wealth and naval and imperial power depended increasingly on sailors' ability to find their way at sea. The standard practice by the sixteenth century was 'dead reckoning'; that is, keeping an account of the direction in which the ship had sailed and an estimate of the distance covered. On a long voyage, however, wind, tides and currents could take a ship miles away from the estimated position, so it was especially important to develop devices to enable the mariner to check his exact location.

In order to 'fix' his position, a navigator needed to be able to check both his latitude – that is, to know how far north or south he was – and his longitude, or east-west position. North of the equator, the height of the Pole Star above the horizon in degrees was roughly the same as the latitude. But this method could not be

**Bronze-mounted lodestone of about 1690**

Until the mid 18th century, when an improved compass was invented (see opposite page), mariners on long voyages had to carry with them a piece of magnetite, or lodestone, to restore the magnetism of the compass needle. The soft iron then used for the needle could carry only a weak magnetism, which faded quite quickly. Lodestones were often mounted in brass, bronze or silver cases, and sometimes had an iron or steel 'keeper', a bar to help preserve their magnetic power. The lodestone was stroked in one direction along the compass needle to re-magnetize it. The lodestone shown is unusually large and weighs 20.25 lbs (9.19 kg).
*NAV0706 [D9252]*

## The most advanced nations are always those who navigate the most.

RALPH WALDO EMERSON, *SOCIETY AND SOLITUDE*, 1870

used close to, or south of, the equator. By the end of the fifteenth century the Portuguese had solved this problem by devising tables of the position of the Sun and adapting the astrolabe, the quadrant and the cross-staff, used in astronomy, to measure its altitude. On ocean voyages, a common method of finding port was to sail north or south until the correct latitude was reached, and then to sail along that latitude to the destination ('latitude sailing').

Early instruments were often difficult to use on the moving deck of a ship and, even in calm weather, not very accurate. Mariners and scholars tried to improve navigational instruments, resulting in the widespread adoption first of the back-staff, invented by John Davis in about 1594, and then of the octant, often known as Hadley's quadrant, after its inventor, John Hadley, who described it to the Royal Society in 1731.

The problem of finding longitude at sea was not solved until the second half of the eighteenth century, when two methods were devised. Both made use of the fact that the Earth rotates on its axis a full 360° in 24 hours. Therefore, an hour's difference in local time between two places is equivalent to 15° of longitude and vice versa. The first way of finding longitude was the 'lunar distance' method, which involved making accurate measurements of the relative positions of the Moon and either the Sun or certain stars, and then using the tables in *The Nautical Almanac*,

**Binnacle to the design patented by Sir William Thomson (later Lord Kelvin) in 1876**
The growing use of iron in the construction of ships, from the late 18th century onwards, affected the accuracy of the compass. Attraction by the iron caused compass needles to deviate from magnetic north in unpredictable ways. The Scottish mathematician and physicist, Sir William Thomson, developed a new compass housing, or binnacle, to overcome this problem, incorporating corrector magnets and iron spheres to counteract the effects of the ship's iron. He also devised a much lighter compass card with two or more short parallel needles, which was less subject to oscillation and wear than the cards previously used.
*AC0036 [C9296]*

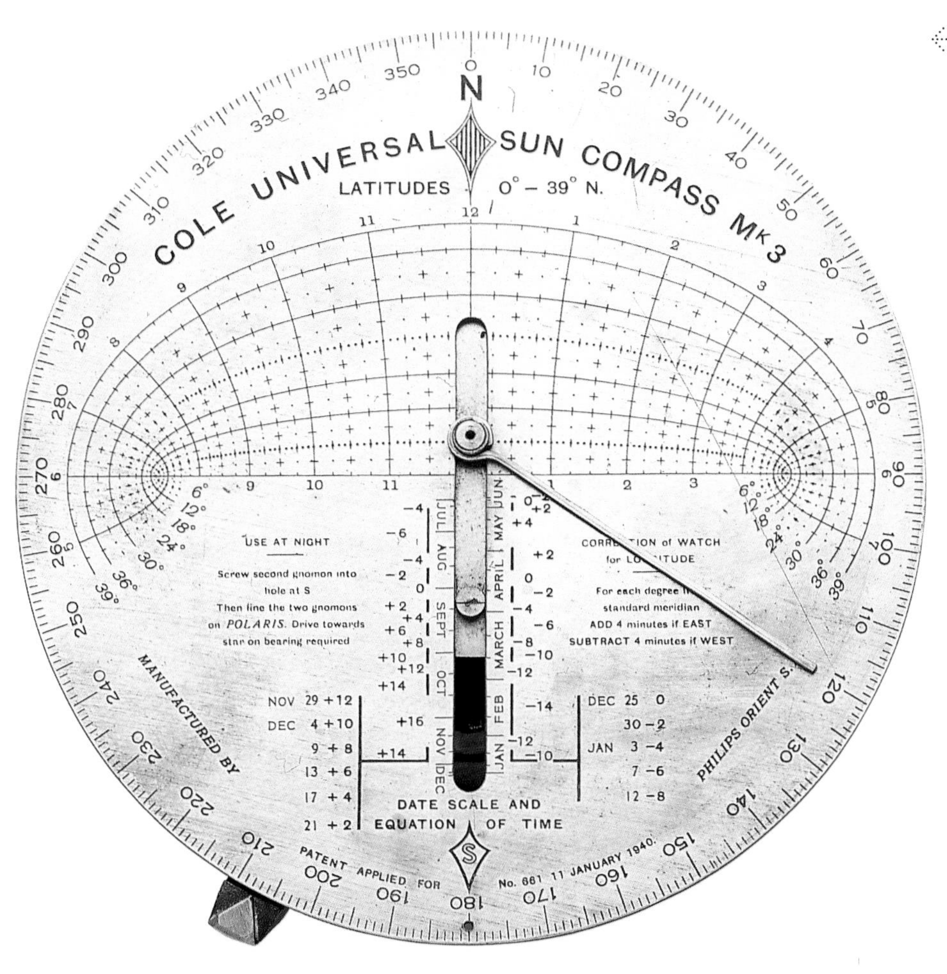


**Cole Universal Sun Compass Mark 3, made by Philips Orient, South Africa, about 1940**

Navigation on land and in the air, like that at sea, made use of the compass. The Museum's collection includes a number of compasses specifically developed for non-maritime use, many of them devised by the Admiralty Compass Observatory, which supplied compasses for the British Army and Air Force as well as the Royal Navy. The sun compass was designed for tank warfare in North Africa during World War II, as magnetic compasses were unreliable inside such vehicles. In this instance, the early experiments were carried out by the Army, and the Compass Observatory became involved later. The ellipses on the dial represent different latitudes, and are crossed by lines for local time.
*NAV0398 [D6264]*

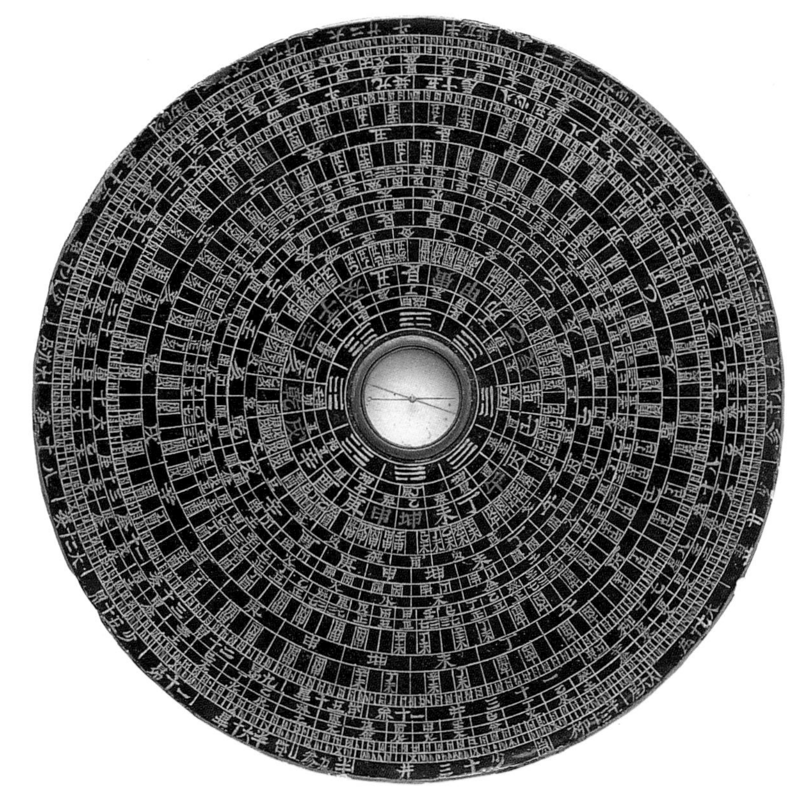

**Chinese geomancer's compass by Chou Hua-Chi, about 1850**

The Greenwich collection includes a number of non-European compasses, some of them designed for uses other than navigation. In China, geomancers used compasses to advise on the best orientation of buildings and graves for good luck. The small compass in the centre is surrounded by circles of Chinese characters for the 24 Chinese compass points, constellations, planets, cycle of years and other matters connected with divination.
*NAV0244 [D6192]*

first published in 1766, and much tedious calculation, to convert the observations into longitude. The second method relied mainly on a very accurate time-keeper, first developed by the Englishman John Harrison between 1730 and 1759 (see Chapter 2), which became known as the marine chronometer. This was kept at the time of the home port, while local time was calculated from observations of the Pole Star or Sun, and the difference between the two converted to longitude.

During the nineteenth century the increasing use of iron in the construction of ships affected the reliability of the magnetic compass. This problem was studied by the seventh Astronomer Royal, Sir George Airy, who made a number of recommendations. A full solution to the problem was eventually found through the work of the Scottish physicist, Sir William Thomson (1824–1907), later Lord Kelvin, who invented a compass binnacle containing corrector magnets, patented in 1876.

After the development of radio transmissions by Marconi from 1895 onwards, experiments began in the use of radio waves for direction-finding at sea, and several systems were developed. *(cont. p. 56)*

**Mariner's astrolabe, Spanish or Portuguese, about 1588**
The mariner's astrolabe was a simplified version of an instrument developed by Arab astronomers for measuring the height of heavenly bodies above the horizon. It was heavier and had portions of the disk cut away to reduce wind resistance, both features helping to keep it steady when used on shipboard. The Pole Star was sighted directly through small pin-holes in the two vanes mounted on the pivoting alidade or rule. The altitude in degrees was then read off from the scale on the outer edge of the instrument. To measure the Sun's position, the astrolabe was held below waist height, the alidade being adjusted so that a beam of sunlight passed through the top pin-hole on to the bottom one. Columbus used a mariner's astrolabe on his voyages to the Americas but this one was found in 1845 under a rock on Valentia Island, close to the point off southern Ireland where three ships of the Spanish Armada were wrecked. The scale lacks numerals so it may be part of unfinished equipment hurried aboard in 1588.
*NAV0022 [C5386]*

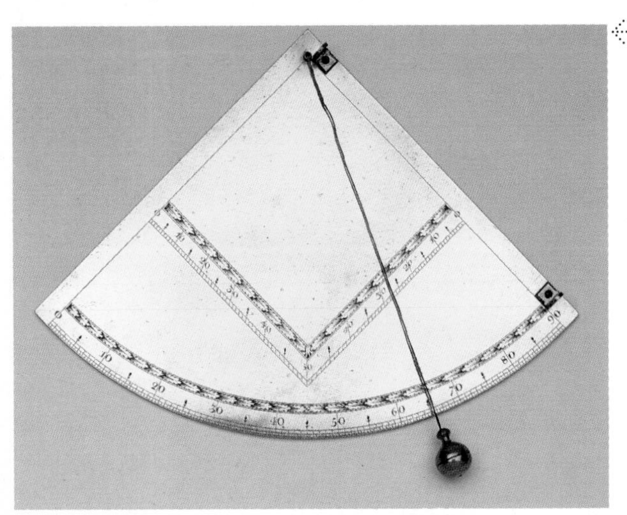

**Mariner's quadrant, English, about 1725**
The quadrant was one of the earliest devices for measuring angles, either of a star above the horizon, or the top of a building or hill in surveying. As its name suggests, it consists of a quarter of a circle, the curved edge being divided into 90° and with a cord and weight suspended from the point of the right-angle. The object was aligned through the sights on one edge, and the angle of elevation read off where the cord crossed the scale. This example is made of brass, with the degree scale subdivided for measurements to 30 minutes of arc, and has a fitted mahogany carrying box.
*NAV1062 [D9253]*

AFRICA

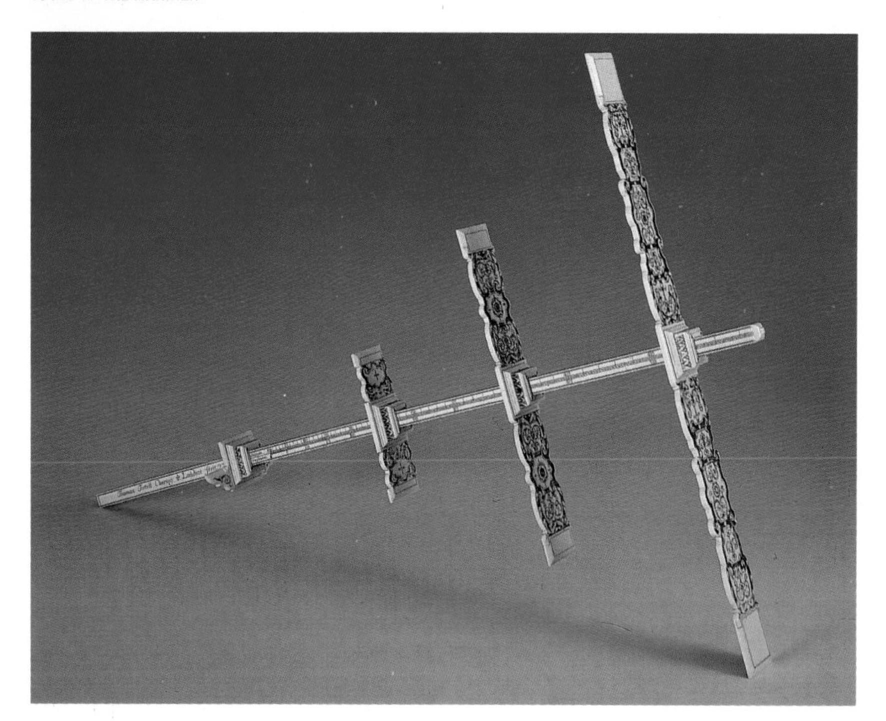

**Cross-staff by Thomas Tuttell of Charing Cross, London, about 1700**
The cross-staff was another device for measuring the altitude of the Sun or Pole Star. It made use of the properties of right-angled triangles, or trigonometry. The observer rested the main staff on the bone just below his eye and moved the cross until the bottom was in line with the horizon, and the top with the lower limb (edge) of the star or Sun, then read off the position on the scale in degrees and minutes. Cross-staves were normally made of wood and few have survived. This one comes from an ivory presentation set of navigational instruments, part of Sir James Caird's huge benefactions to the Museum. Only one of the three cross-pieces shown was used at a time, depending on the altitude being measured.
*NAV0505 [D4690]*

The art of navigation demonstrateth
how by the shortest good way,
by the aptest direction, and in the shortest time,
a sufficient ship ... be conducted.

DR JOHN DEE, MATHEMATICIAN AND ASTROLOGER, 1570

**Back-staff, William Garner, London, 1734**
The back-staff was invented by Captain John Davis in about 1594, to overcome the problems he had with glare when taking sights in the Arctic with an astrolabe or cross-staff. With his back to the Sun, the observer sighted the horizon through a hole in a vane on the large arc and the horizontal slitted vane, which was fitted at the other end of the instrument. A vane on the smaller arc cast a shadow on the horizon vane, where it was aligned with the image seen through the slit. When it was too hazy for shadows the lens was used on the small arc to create a point of light from the Sun to align with the horizon. The observer worked out the Sun's altitude by adding the values shown by the shadow and sighting vanes on their respective scales. The instrument was also know as the Davis or English quadrant. The one shown here is signed *Made by Will Garner for Oliver Thomson.*
*NAV0041 [D6415]*

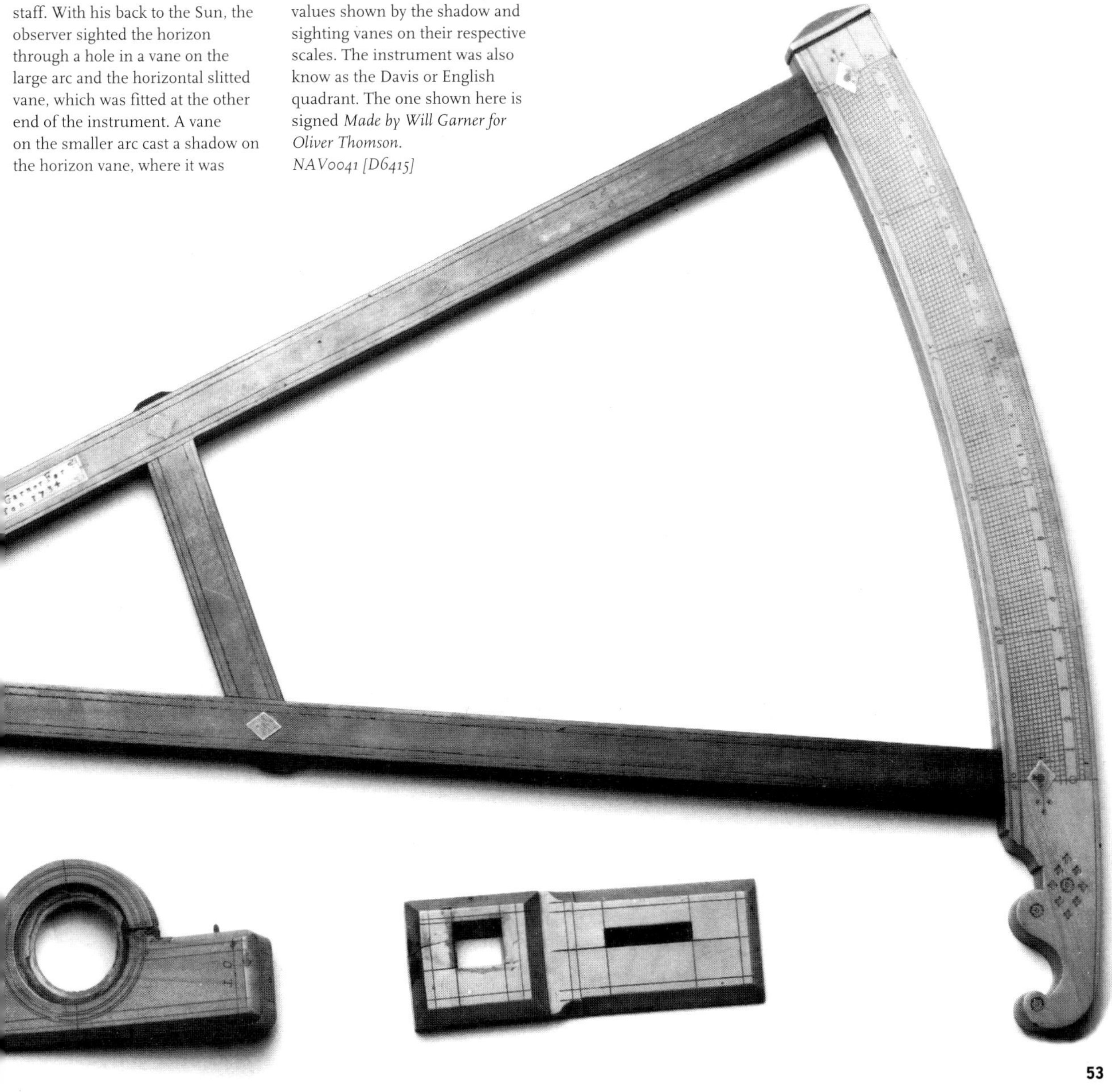

**Sextant by John and Edward Troughton, London, about 1797**
The sextant takes its name from its shape, a sixth of a circle. Astronomical sextants had been in use since the 16th century but the marine version was developed in about 1757 by Captain John Campbell with the help of the instrument-maker John Bird. It worked on exactly the same principle as the octant but, having a longer scale, could be used for angles up to 120°. This example has the double frame patented by Edward Troughton in 1788, which provided rigidity without too much weight. It was given as a presentation piece and bears the inscription *The Gift of Capt Jas Brisbane to Mr. T. H. Hoskins Master of H. M. Ship Saturn 1802.* *NAV1139 [D6085]*

**Octant by Benjamin Martin, London, about 1760**
The octant greatly improved the accuracy of navigational observations at sea by using mirrors to bring a reflected image of the star or Sun alongside the horizon, when viewed through the sight. Its great advantage was that this meant it did not have to be held absolutely still to obtain an accurate reading. Although the principle had been explained by Sir Isaac Newton, the form used at sea was first demonstrated to the Royal Society in 1731 by John Hadley. This example is made of mahogany and has an ivory scale and brass index arm, with a vernier for measurements to one minute of arc. As its name implies, an octant forms an eighth of a circle but the use of reflection doubles the angle, so that the scale reads to 90°. It has a radius of $17\frac{3}{4}$ inches (441 mm). Later octants were often made of ebony and had a smaller radius. *NAV1254 [D9250]*

**Artificial horizon by Elliott Brothers, London, 1861**

When a sextant or similar instrument was used on land to measure the altitude of a heavenly body, an artificial horizon was needed. The simplest and oldest form was a metal or wooden trough into which mercury was poured, to create a flat reflective surface. A glass lid prevented the wind from disturbing the mercury. This example is made of iron, with an iron bottle for storing the mercury when not in use. The whole set packs into a mahogany box and originally belonged to Queen Victoria's second son, the lid being marked with a crown and the inscription *Alfred 1861*. It was presented to the Museum in 1936 by one of its great early supporters, Queen Mary.
*NAV0003 [D6397-2]*

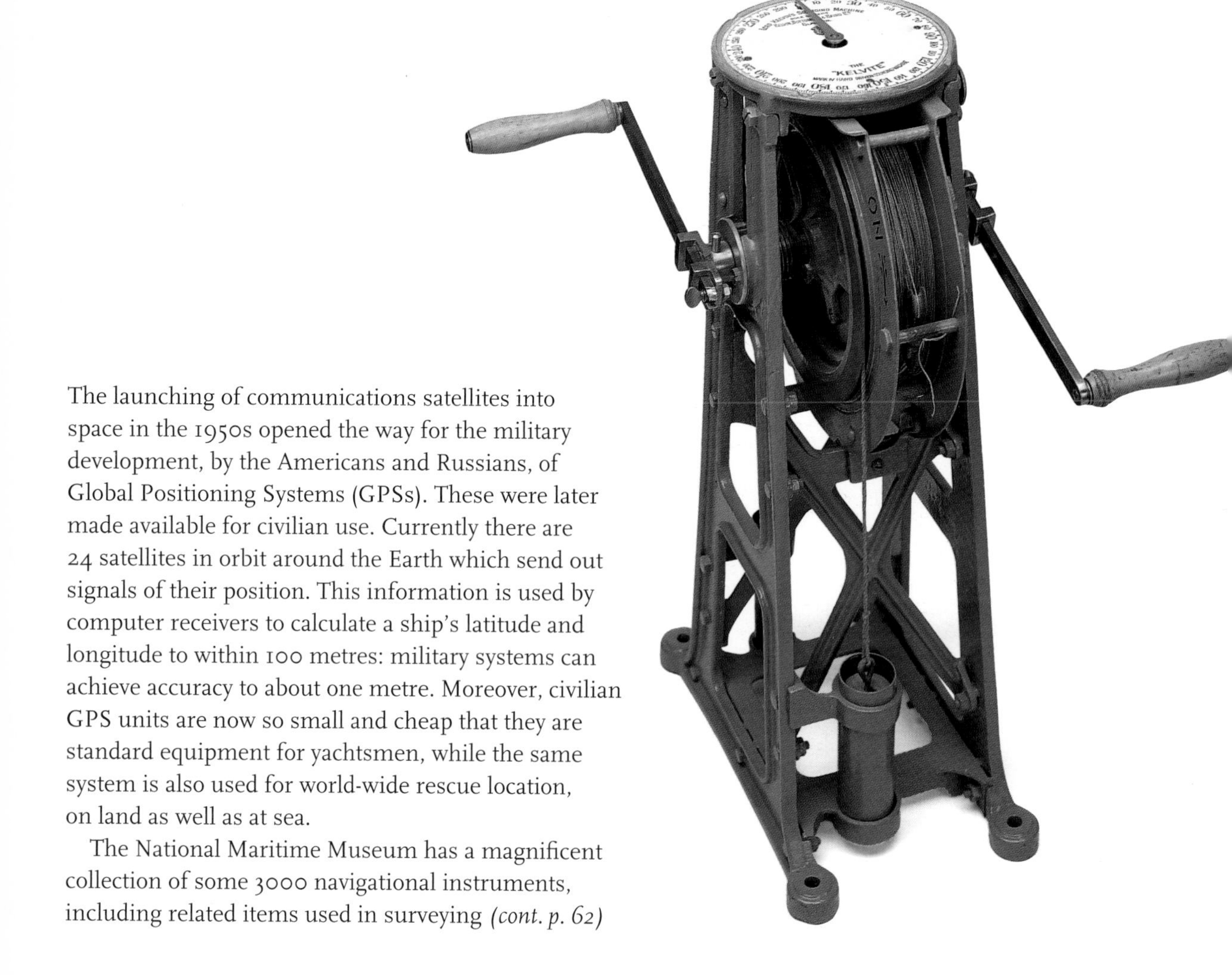


The launching of communications satellites into space in the 1950s opened the way for the military development, by the Americans and Russians, of Global Positioning Systems (GPSs). These were later made available for civilian use. Currently there are 24 satellites in orbit around the Earth which send out signals of their position. This information is used by computer receivers to calculate a ship's latitude and longitude to within 100 metres: military systems can achieve accuracy to about one metre. Moreover, civilian GPS units are now so small and cheap that they are standard equipment for yachtsmen, while the same system is also used for world-wide rescue location, on land as well as at sea.

The National Maritime Museum has a magnificent collection of some 3000 navigational instruments, including related items used in surveying *(cont. p. 62)*

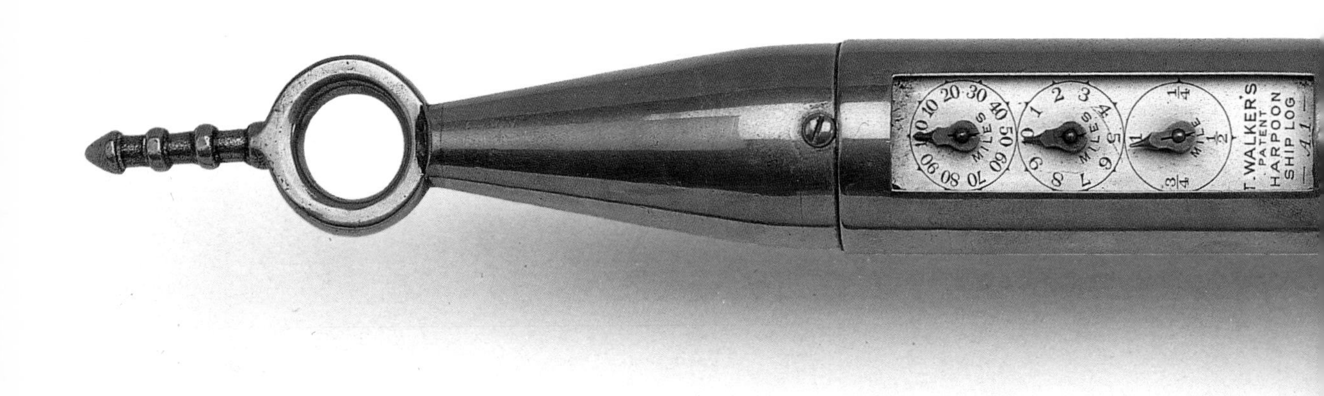

Navigation is the Science of finding a ship's position, and the art of conducting her safely from place to place.

ADMIRALTY MANUAL OF NAVIGATION, 1954

**Kelvite Mark IV sounding machine, by Kelvin, Bottomley and Baird, Glasgow, about 1930**
The earliest method of measuring the depth of water underneath a ship was with a line and a lead weight but it was very time-consuming. During the 19th century there were a number of attempts to mechanize the process. The first commercially successful device was patented by Edward Massey in 1802. An improved sounding machine by Sir William Thomson (Lord Kelvin) received a patent in 1876 and was still being produced with only minor modifications in the 1960s. It used piano wire wound on to a drum, fitted with winding handles and a brake, together with a glass tube lined inside with a substance which changed colour on contact with water. As the tube was lowered increasing pressure pushed the water further up and when it was recovered the depth was read off against a scale.
*NAV0686 [D9242]*

**Patent ship's log, by Edward Massey, London, about 1840**
In the 16th century, British mariners used a piece of wood, called a log or log-ship, to help them estimate their speed. The log, attached to a line with knots at regular intervals, was thrown astern and the rope payed out for a short time, often 30 seconds, to estimate speed in nautical miles per hour. This was the origin of expressing speed in 'knots'. Attempts were made from the 16th century onwards to devise a mechanical log which would automatically record speed or distance, but the first commercially successful version was patented by Thomas Massey in 1802. It consisted of a brass rotator linked to a geared mechanical recording mechanism. This example was owned by John Lort Stokes, who was Assistant Surveyor on the *Beagle* on the voyage on which Charles Darwin served as naturalist.
*NAV0724 [D5333]*

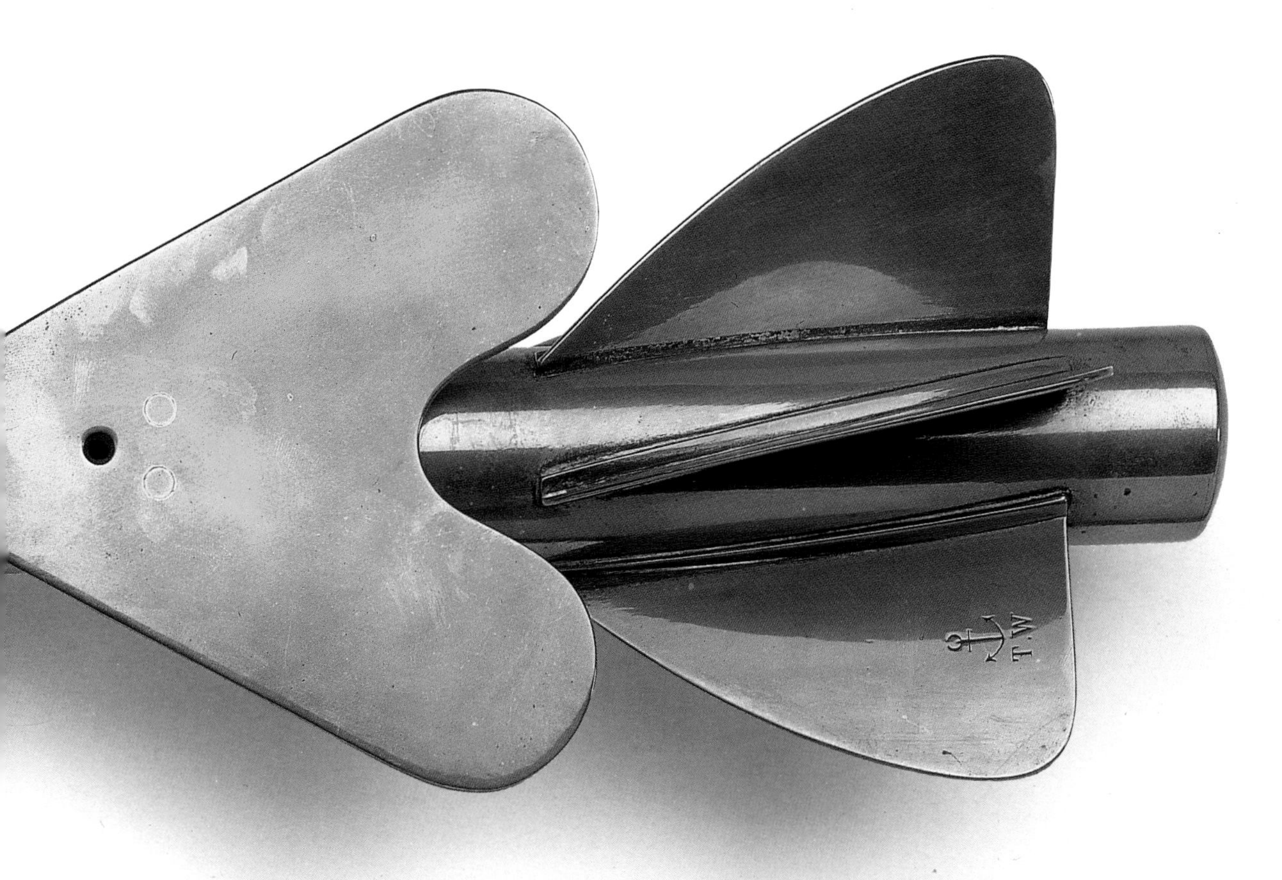

**Traverse board, probably German or Scandinavian, about 1800**
Simple traverse boards were in use in northern Europe by the 16th century. They had a series of holes along lines marking the 32 points of the compass. Pegs were attached to the board by string and placed in the correct hole for the course being steered, normally one hole for each half hour of the watch, as measured by a sand-glass. Later versions, such as the example shown here, also had a series of holes along the bottom for speed, taken by the log and line. At the end of each watch the records were written down, usually by the ship's master, and the pegs pulled out ready for the next watch.
*NAV1698 [A5136]*

**Battenberg's course indicator by Elliott Brothers (London) Ltd, about 1925**
Station, speed and distance indicators were developed from the mid 19th century. With the introduction of fast steamships, it became more important to be able to calculate the course and speed of other vessels within sight. This device was developed by Prince Louis of Battenberg, First Sea Lord at the outbreak of World War I. The outer edge is marked in compass points and degrees. The guide's bar, with the large pointer, is set to the compass course of the guide ship. The bar pivoted at the centre of the small circle has a scale for speed and the other two bars have scales for distance. The device proved especially useful in wartime convoys for maintaining station on another ship.
*NAV0172 [D9249]*

**Set of Napier's bones, English, about 1679**
The Scottish mathematician, John Napier (1550–1617), who first devised tables of logarithms, also invented a series of wooden rods bearing tables of multiples, which made long multiplication and division a relatively simple matter of addition or subtraction. They were nicknamed 'Napier's bones'. This set is made of boxwood and the rods are fitted into a small carrying case, only 5 inches (127 mm) long, in such a way that they can be turned by using the knobs on the outside. The set was probably intended for nautical use, as the box is engraved with a tide table and a perpetual calendar.
*NAV0126 [D7195]*

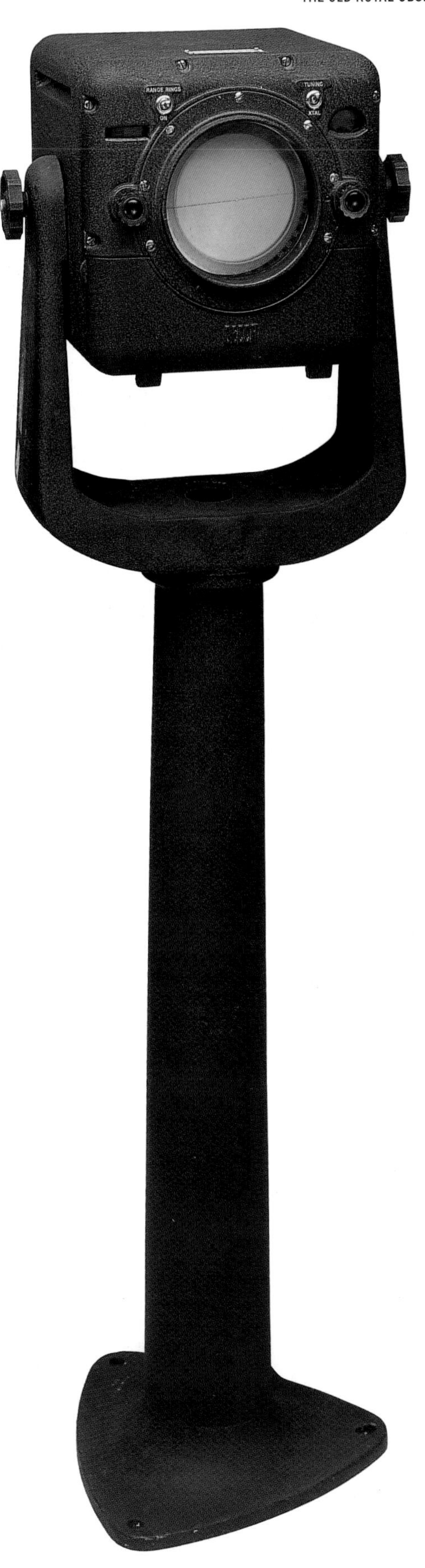


**Early marine radar by Decca Radar Ltd, 1949**
Radar – the initial letters of Radio Detection And Ranging – was first developed with great success in Britain during World War II, 1939–45. At sea, it could be used for position finding and to provide warning of approaching ships or hazards. Radar uses very high-frequency radio waves which are transmitted by a continuously rotating scanner mounted high on the ship. If the radio waves strike a solid object, or rainstorm, they are bounced back to the scanner, interpreted, and the output displayed on a screen on the bridge.
*NAV1064 [D9243]*

**Theodolite** (left) **by J. Sisson, London, about 1737;** (right) **by Dollond, London, about 1840**

The theodolite was invented in the 16th century and by the end of the 18th century was regarded as the most important surveying instrument. It enables the user to measure, at the same time, the horizontal angle between two points and their angles of elevation. These examples are made of brass. The horizontal circle and vertical semi-circle are both divided into degrees, with verniers for subdivision into minutes of arc. The Dollond example has microscopes for reading the verniers and both have telescopes for sighting and a compass for orientation. The Dollond family established a leading firm of optical instrument makers, which they controlled from 1750 to 1870.

*NAV1451 and NAV1461 [C8929]*

> The fair breeze blew, the white foam flew
> The furrow followed free;
> We were the first that ever burst
> into that silent sea.
>
> SAMUEL TAYLOR COLERIDGE, *THE RIME OF THE ANCIENT MARINER*, 1798

and chart work. The collections include all the major types of navigational instrument, with objects from many cultures and dating from the Middle Ages to the present day. They can be divided into six main groups:

- Direction-finding: compasses and their accessories
- Devices for measuring the altitude of heavenly bodies
- Depth-sounding
- Estimating, calculating and recording speed and distance
- Aids to calculation
- Modern radio aids to navigation

In addition there are surveying instruments, used in mapping and charting, and equipment used for meteorology and oceanography. There are also optical instruments used for making observations, aids to calculation, and drawing instruments used for plotting a course or recording the results of survey.

*Gloria Clifton, Curator of Navigational Sciences*

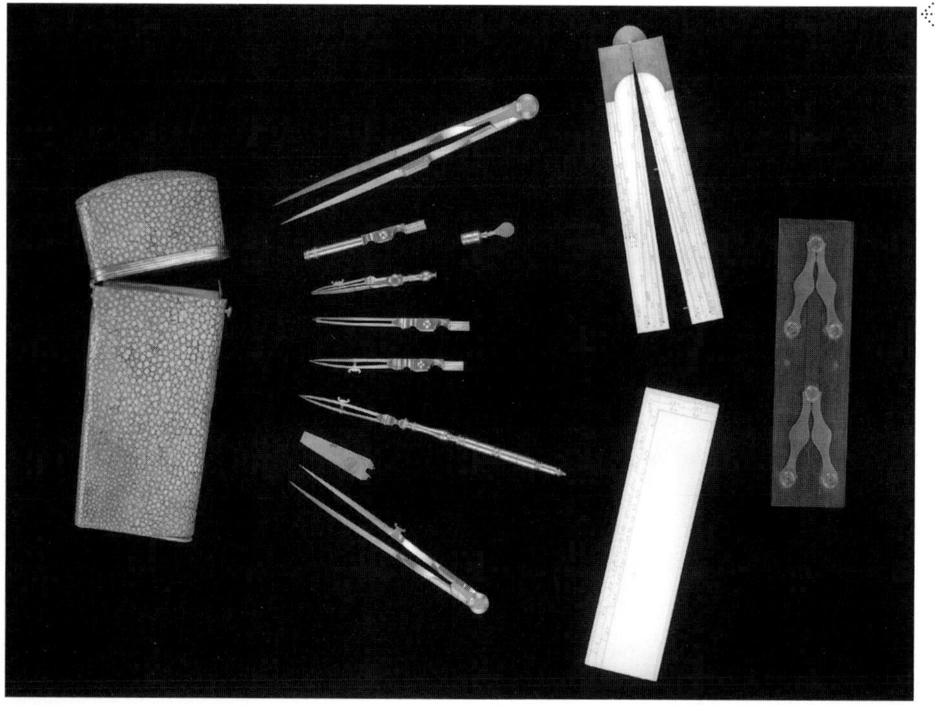

**A set of drawing instruments in a pocket case, by George Adams Junior, London, about 1780**
The set consists of brass and steel compasses, pens, dividers, ivory sector and protractor, and an ebony parallel rule. There are twelve pieces in total, all of which fit into slots in the silver and shagreen, or ray-skin, case. Such sets of instruments were used by architects, navigators and surveyors as well as mathematicians. The two George Adams, father and son, were leading London mathematical instrument makers of the 18th century, with a shop in Fleet Street.
*NAV0651 [D1865-B]*

**Hand-held telescope by W. C. Cox of Devonport, about 1840**
A typical telescope of the kind used in the 19th century for observation at sea, this is a refractor, that is, the observer views directly through the small eye-glass and larger objective lens. The draw tube and fittings are brass and the barrel is covered with leather, decorated with a printed chart of signalling flags. It has a focal length of 28½ inches (724 mm) and an objective lens of 1¼ inches diameter (43 mm). This example, by a Plymouth maker, W. C. Cox of Devonport, once belonged to John Lort Stokes, Assistant Surveyor under Captain Fitzroy on the *Beagle* on the voyage which inspired Charles Darwin's *Origin of Species*.
*NAV1670 [D9288]*

**Marine cistern barometer by Negretti & Zambra, London, about 1916**
Negretti & Zambra were among the best known London manufacturers of meteorological instruments by the late 19th century. This Meteorological Office standard, Fortin-type, mercury barometer with a thermometer, is made of black-painted brass, with a silvered scale. In about 1800 Nicolas Fortin of Paris had devised a barometer in which the surface of the mercury could be adjusted to touch a fixed reference point, which made it easier to obtain an accurate reading. Barometers measure atmospheric pressure and had been carried on ships since the 18th century. A 'falling glass' – dropping pressure – heralds bad weather; a 'rising' one, good.
*NAV0781 [D1326] l*

**Tide gauge by T. Kent, London and Luton, about 1926**
This type of clockwork tide gauge provides a permanent record of the height of the water over time, by tracing a line on a roll of paper wrapped round the cylinder. The device is made of brass and steel, with an enamelled clock dial. It was used immediately downstream of Richmond Lock on the River Thames between 1926 and 1962, and was presented to the Museum by the Port of London Authority.
*NAV0995 [D9282]*

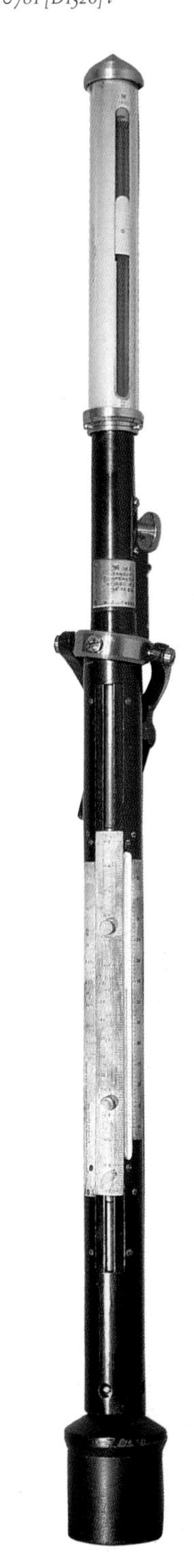

# CHAPTER FOUR

# MAPPING THE OCEANS

## *Sea Charts and Atlases*

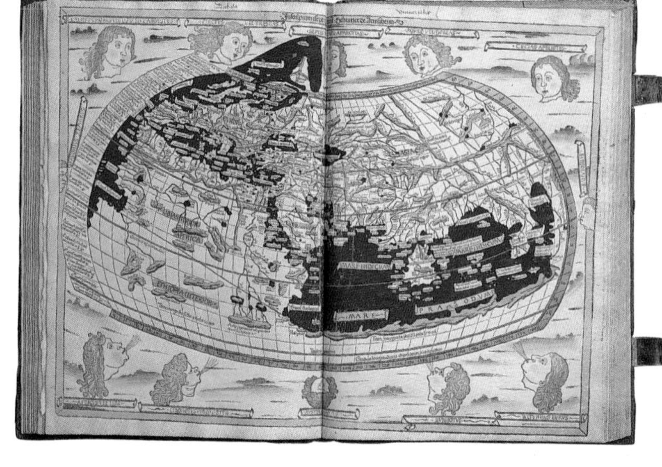

**World map, from a Ptolemy's Cosmographia, 1482**
The Alexandrian astronomer Ptolemy (4th century BC), is famous for his treatise, the *Almagest*, which describes the 'Ptolemaic' system of the universe in which the Earth is at the centre. He was also a skilled geographer and mathematician and the first to plot a globe using a latitude and longitude grid-system. In Roman times his work was forgotten and was only rediscovered during the Renaissance. Many editions of his *Cosmographia* were printed from 1475 until the 18th century. This edition of his world map, published in Ulm, shows the latitude and longitude scale, with Africa appearing as an extension of a vast southern land, and the Indian Ocean as a large expanse of inland water.
*E5109 (C8584)*

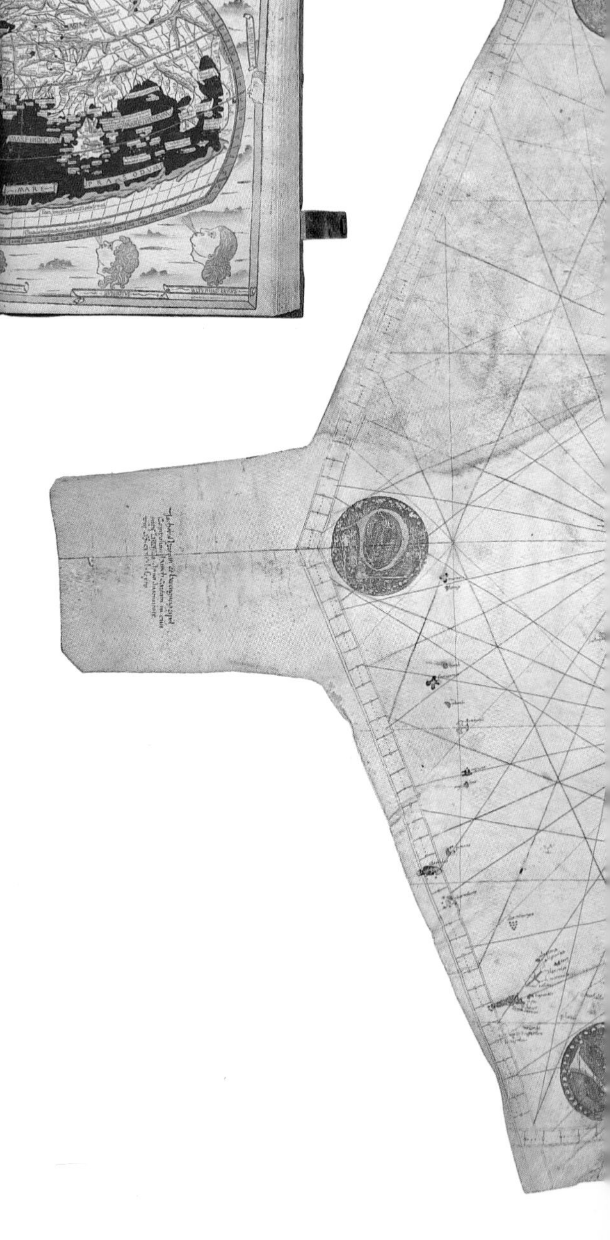

A chart is a representation of an area of sea or ocean, specially prepared to serve the navigational requirements of sailors. Generally drawn on the Mercator projection, which transforms the curved surface of the Earth to a flat plane, a chart contains details of coastlines and islands as well as information on depths and safe anchorages, hazards such as rocks, sandbanks, shoals and wrecks, and the positions of buoys and lighthouses.

Charts and land maps are very ancient. The first maps are believed to have existed in China around 2000 BC. An Egyptian papyrus map from 1300 BC and a Babylonian world map on a clay tablet dating to 600 BC still survive. The Greeks made many advances in map-making. The philosopher Pythagoras (sixth century BC) was the first to introduce the theory that the Earth was round rather than flat. Around 241 BC, Eratosthenes used geometry to calculate the circumference of the Earth to within 200 miles by

**Portulan chart of the Mediterranean, North Atlantic and Black Sea, by Jacobo Bertran and Berenguer Ripol of Barcelona, 1456**
This is the oldest chart in the Museum's collection and typical of portulans of the 15th to 17th centuries. It is hand drawn and coloured on vellum with the characteristic system of rhumb lines and compass roses. These lines served a dual purpose: first, the cartographer used them to construct the chart when drawing the coastlines; later, the sailor used them to plot his course, estimating by dead reckoning the distance and compass-bearing sailed. Images of important cities and national flags are also given, but an unusual feature is the four wind discs situated in each corner of the chart. Also, following the convention of the age, the Red Sea is actually shown in that colour!
*G230:1/7 [3089]*

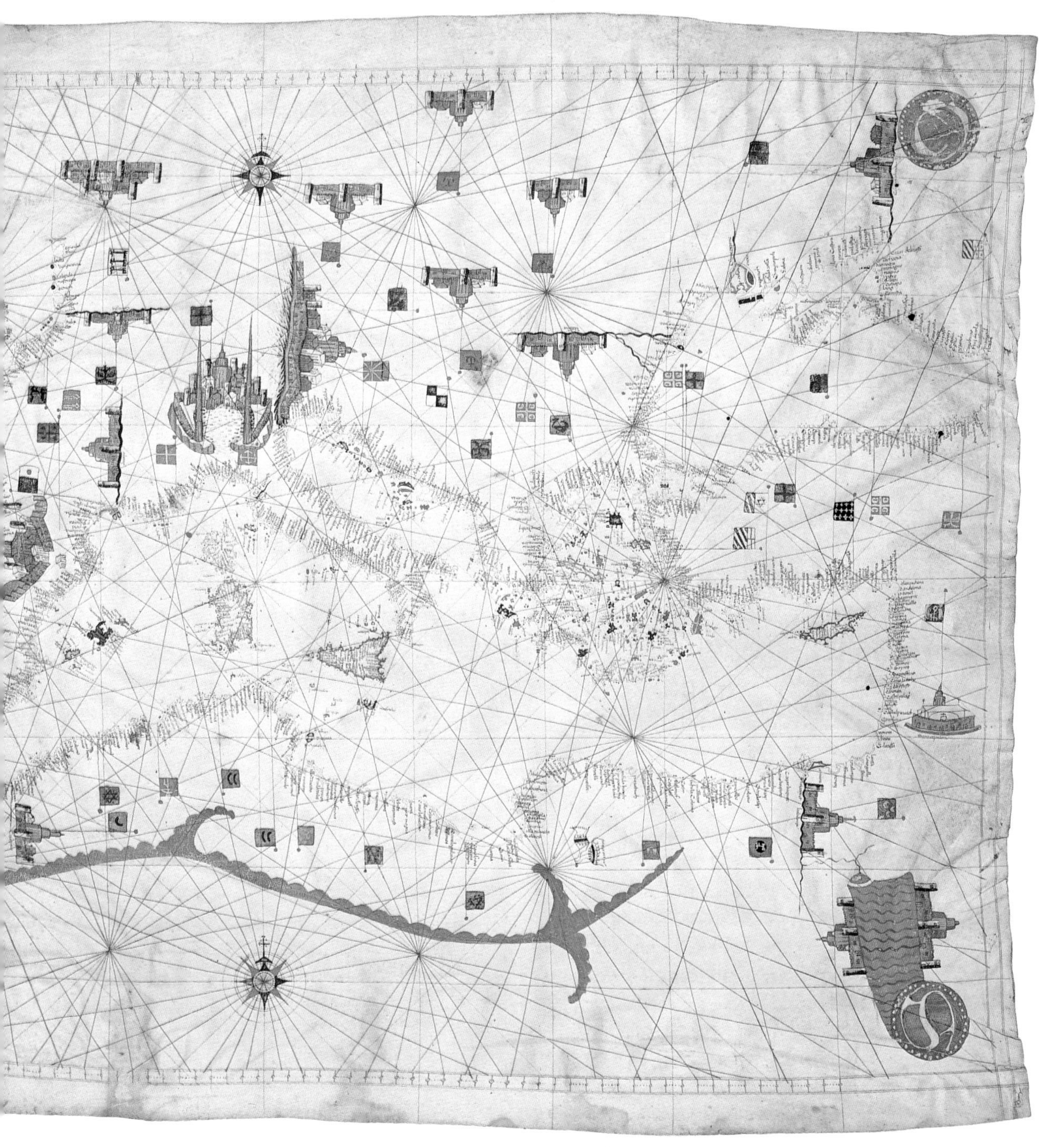

'What's the good of Mercator's North Poles
and Equators, Tropics, Zones and Merdian Lines?'
So the Bellman would cry:
and the crew would reply
'They are merely conventional signs!'

LEWIS CARROLL, *THE HUNTING OF THE SNARK*, 1876

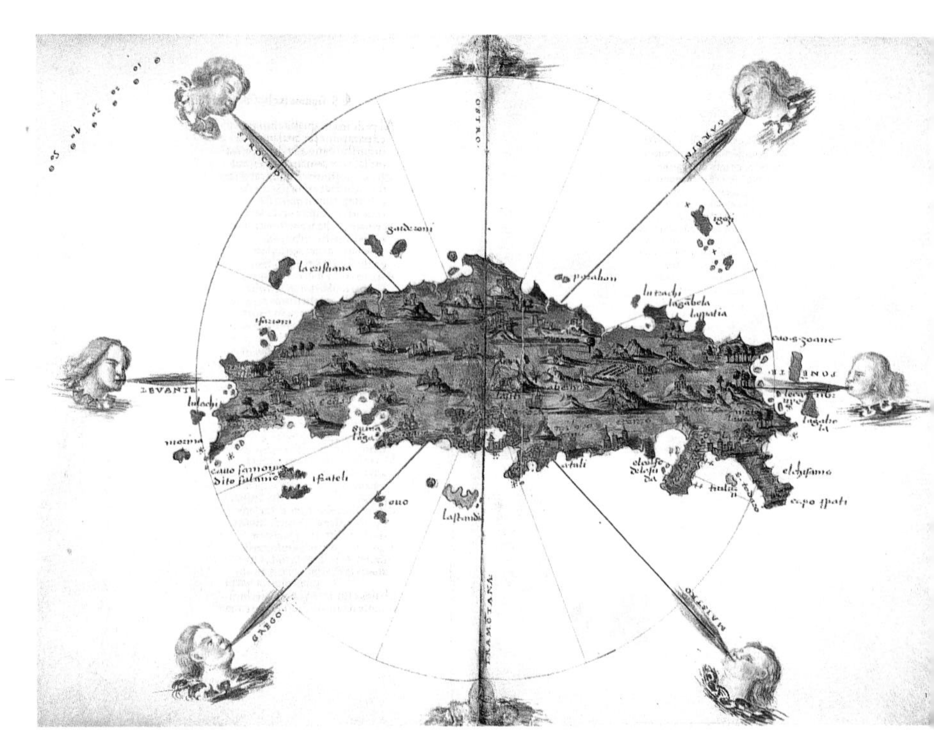

**Chart of Crete by Bartolommeo dalli Sonetti, about 1485**
Early written sailing directions of the Mediterranean were known as portulans. A variation of these was the *isolario* or island book. Bartolommeo Zamberti, a Venetian sailor of the 15th century who generally called himself Bartolommeo dalli Sonetti, was the author of the first printed *isolario*, around 1485, in which, as 'Sonetti' implies, he wrote the descriptions in verse! This primarily covered the islands of the Aegean, but including Crete and Cyprus. This chart comes from a fine manuscript copy of his book and includes an eight-pointed Mediterranean compass rose and representations of the prevailing winds.
*P.21 (D266-9)*

measuring the height of the Sun at the summer solstice at two different cities, Alexandria and Syene (Aswan). Just over 300 years later, Ptolemy developed three different map projections which enabled him to draw recognizable images of the world on a flat surface, with a latitude and longitude scale. The first acknowledged maker of sea charts was Marinus of Tyre, in about AD 100. The oldest surviving chart is, however, the *Carta Pisana*, which dates to about 1275–90.

Early charts were hand-drawn on vellum, and contained carefully positioned wind or compass roses from which projected a network of 'rhumb lines' along which a navigator could plot a course. These charts were known as 'portulans', and developed from portolani, or books of sailing directions. They concentrated on the Mediterranean where a flourishing chart-making industry was established

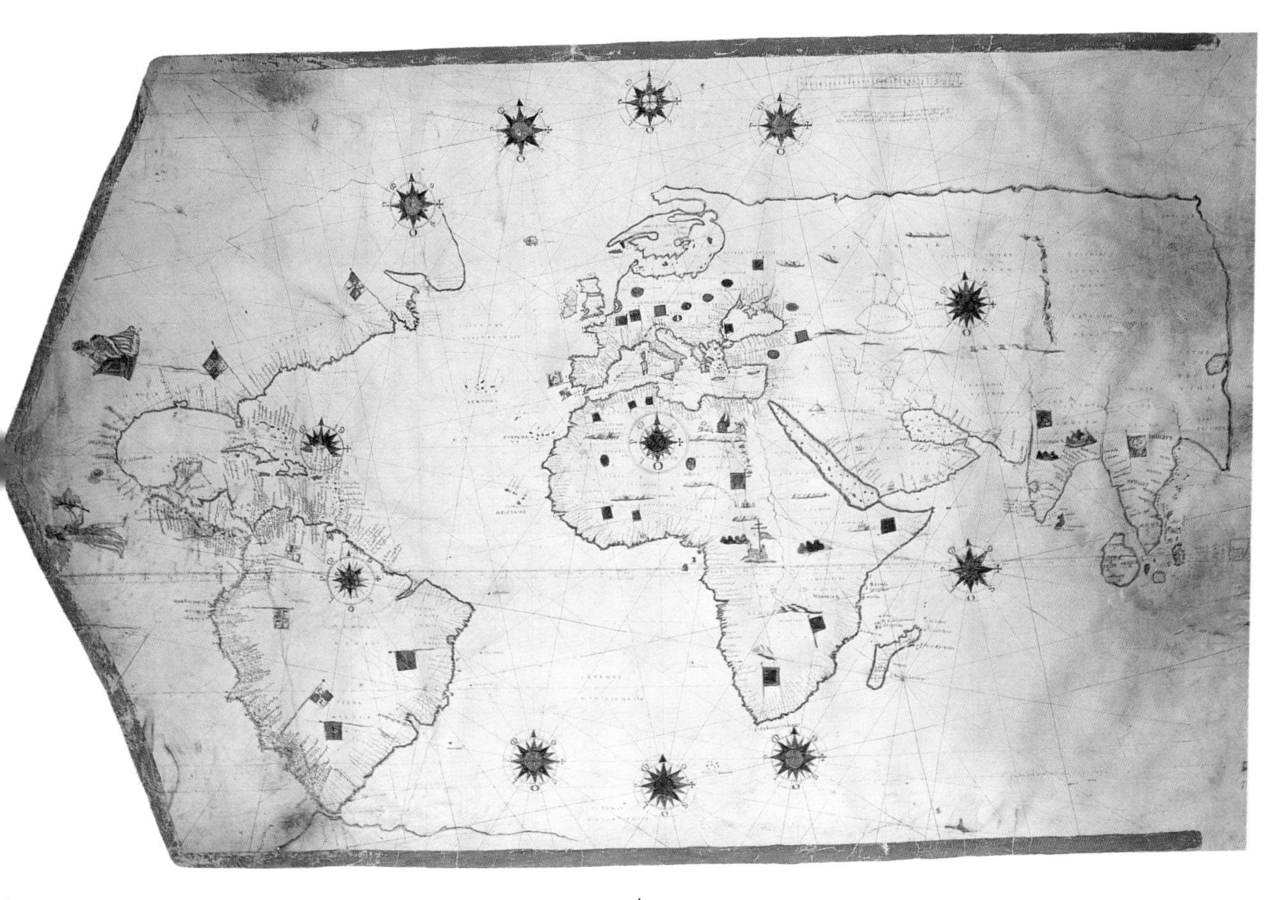

**Portulan map of the world, attributed to Girolamo Verrazano, 1529, corrected to 1540**
This unsigned world map on vellum is believed to be the work of the Florentine cartographer, Girolamo Verrazano, who, with his brother Giovanni, undertook three expeditions to the east coast of America in 1524, 1527 and 1528. Financed by King Francis I of France, they tried to discover a new passage linking the Atlantic and Pacific Oceans. The enterprise failed in 1528 when Giovanni Verrazano was killed and eaten by cannibals in the West Indies – a horrible event witnessed by his brother. This map includes all the information obtained on the brothers' voyages as well as some from earlier Portuguese and Spanish voyages. Note the non-existent Sea of Verrazano, which the brothers thought was an ocean dividing North America. They actually saw the Pamlico Sound.
*G201:1/15 (B6376)*

**Portulan chart of the Atlantic (detail), attributed to Pedro Reinel, about 1535**
Pedro Reinel and his son Jorge were prominent Portuguese cartographers around 1500. Although unsigned, this vellum chart is thought to be Pedro's work and is a fine example of the high standard of Portuguese chart-making of the time. With one exception, the Portuguese and Spanish flags shown are all located on the correct side of the Atlantic demarcation line, 370 leagues west of Cape Verde, by which the Pope divided the unknown world between those two countries under the Treaty of Tordesillas in 1493. On the West Africa coast is a representation of the great Portuguese slaving fortress of El Mina, in modern Ghana.
*G213:2/4 (1478)*

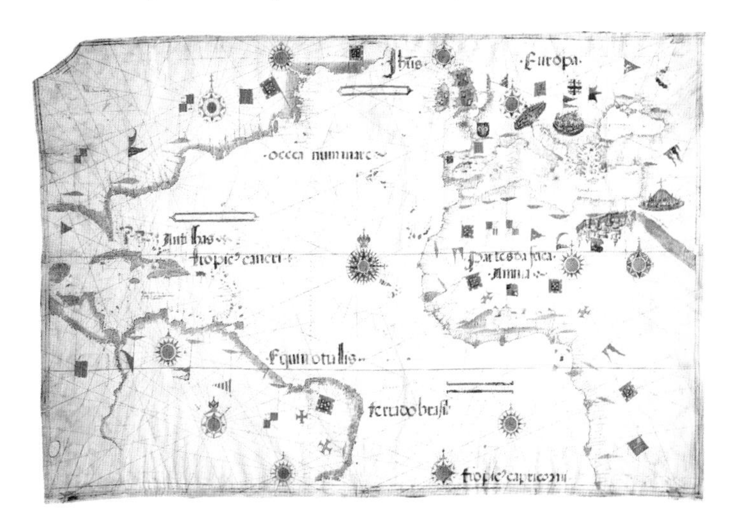

**Printed world map by Gerard Mercator, 1595**

In 1569, the Flemish geographer Gerard Mercator devised the map projection for which he is best known – the Mercator projection. This was a world map in which the parallels of latitude and meridians of longitude appeared as straight lines, intersecting at right angles. This arrangement allowed a navigator to plot his course on a straight line rather than along one that was curved. The main disadvantage of Mercator's projection proved to be the distortion of land areas to the far north and south of the equator. Mercator also prepared a collection of country maps, intended for a volume called *Atlas Sive Cosmographicae Meditationes*, but he died before its completion. This atlas, from which the map shown comes, was finally published in 1595 by his son Rumold. *(D7623) [D9258]*

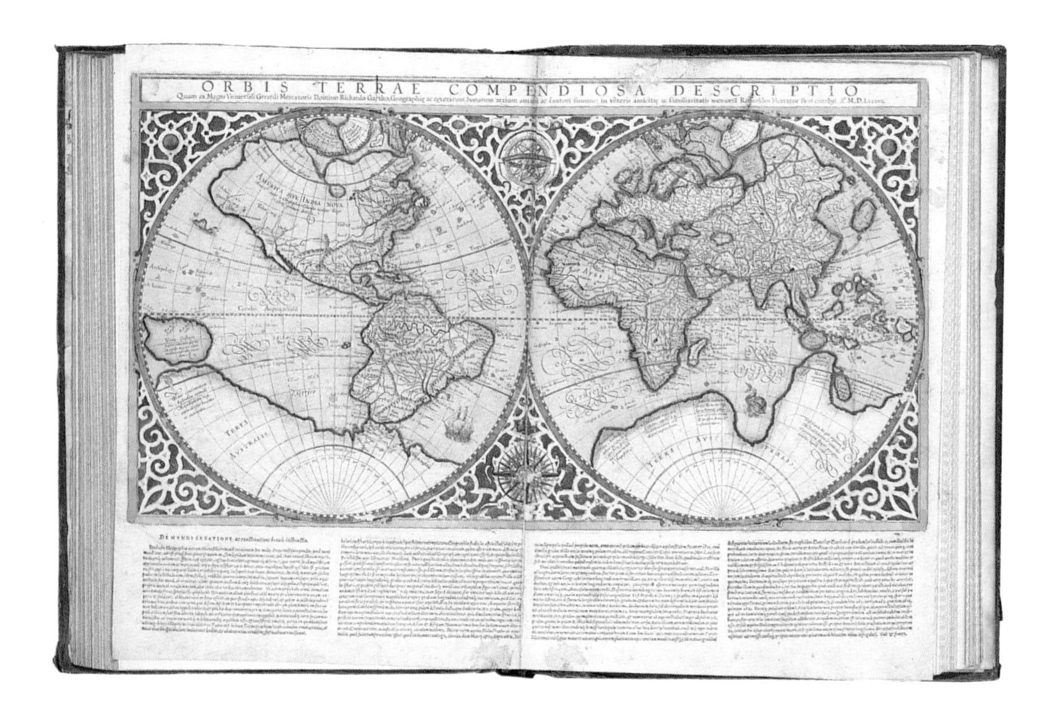


**Printed world map by Abraham Ortelius, 1570**

Antwerp-born Ortelius was a close friend of Gerard Mercator, both being great names in the annals of map-making. His most celebrated achievement was the publication of his *Theatrum Orbis Terrarum* or 'Theatre of the World' in 1570, from which this map comes. The atlas contains maps of different countries and was the first to be widely available. Subsequent editions were improved, enlarged and translated into seven different languages. They were available until 1612, with a smaller version continuing to 1697. The *Typus Orbis Terrarum* includes the 'as yet unknown southern land', *Terra Australis Nondum Cognita*. The non-existence of this mythical continent was finally demonstrated by Captain Cook in the 1770s. *D7643 (C8159)*

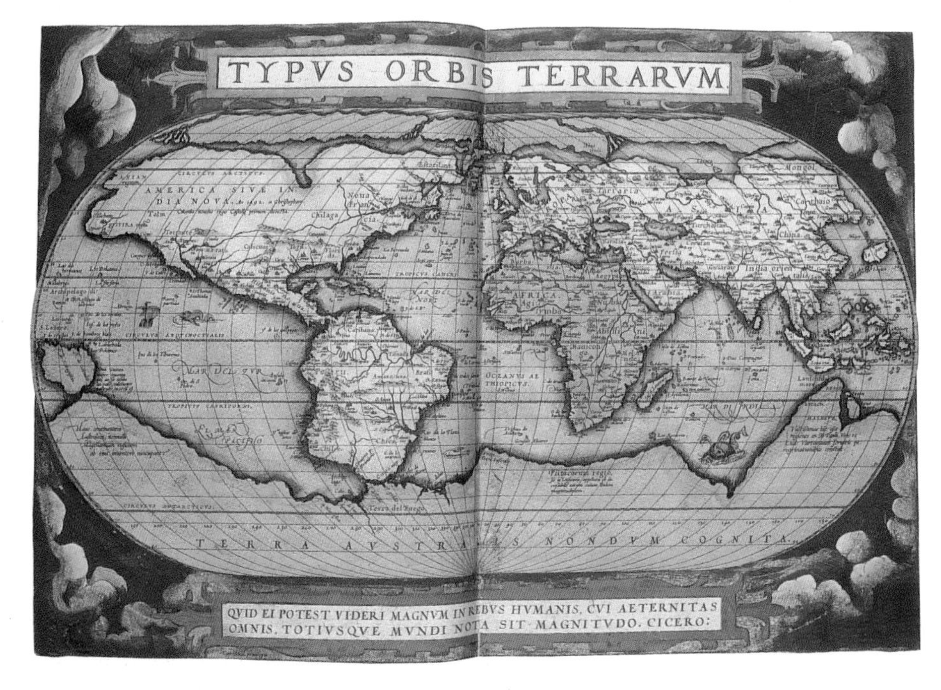

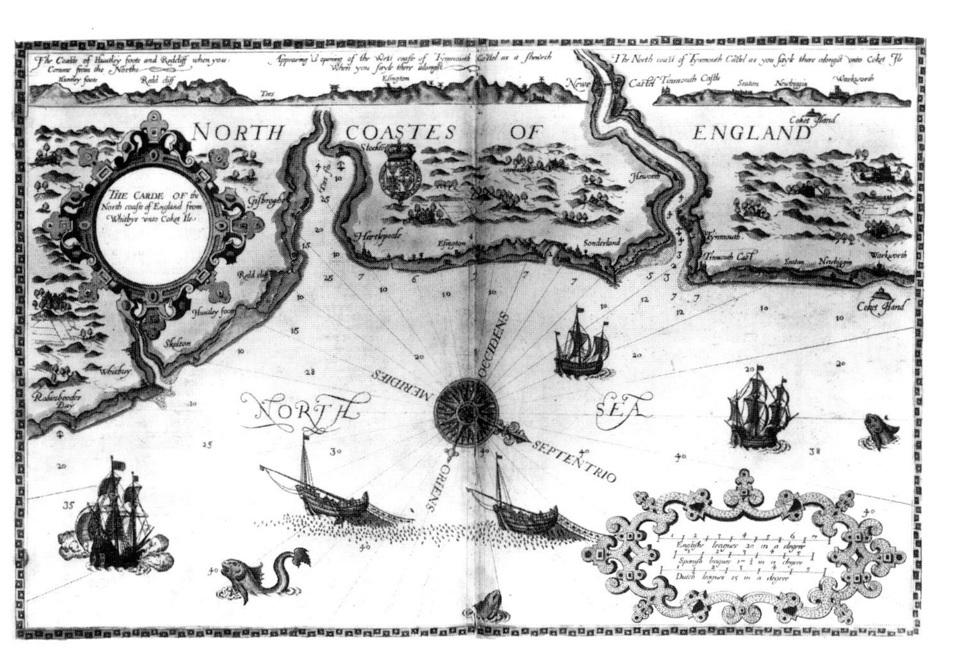


**Printed chart of the north coast of England, from Whitby to Coquet Island, by Lucas Janszoon Waghenaer, 1588**
Waghenaer, a Dutch pilot and hydrographer, produced the first printed sea-atlas of Europe, from the Baltic Sea to the Straits of Gibraltar. This, *De Spieghel der Zeevaert*, was first published in 1584, and contained charts, sailing directions and other navigational information such as soundings and hazards. Large-scale details of harbours and river entrances were also provided to assist seamen. Waghenaer's atlas was subsequently translated into several languages including French, Latin and German, and continued to be published until 1612. The very attractive chart shown is from the English version, entitled *The Mariners Mirrour* (a near translation of the Dutch original), which appeared in 1588.
*D8264 (9578)*

in Genoa and Venice during the thirteenth and fourteenth centuries.

From the early fifteenth century, Portugal emerged as a leading chart-making nation. This was mainly due to the influence of Prince Henry the Navigator, who founded a school of astronomy, cartography and navigation at Sagres in 1437. He is best remembered as a patron of exploration.

The years around 1500 are known as the great age of exploration with Columbus 'discovering' the Americas for Spain in 1492 and Vasco da Gama opening the sea route to India in 1498 on behalf of the Portuguese. Subsequent charts recorded the results of these voyages, and both Portugal and Spain established 'hydrographic' offices in the early sixteenth century: the former was the Casa da India in Lisbon, and the latter the Casa de Contracción in Seville. Many Italian, Spanish, and Portuguese charts survive from this exciting era.

The late 1500s saw the appearance of three of the most important developments in the history of cartography (the mapping of land features) and hydrography (mapping the oceans). First, in 1569, was the issue of a world map by Gerard Mercator, on which the parallels of latitude and meridians of longitude were drawn as straight lines and crossed at right angles. This famous Mercator's projection enabled a mariner to sail on a straight rhumb (a course line) rather than one that was curved. But despite the advantages of Mercator's system, the compass or plane chart continued to be used at sea and, surprisingly, his projection was not used on a chart until 1646–47.

# Thence Home: and took my Lord Sandwich's draught of the harbour of Portsmouth down to Ratcliffe to one Burston, to make a plat [chart] for the King, and another for the Duke, and another for himself, which will be very neat.

SAMUEL PEPYS, *DIARY*, 18 FEBRUARY 1665

In 1570, Abraham Ortelius published the first edition of his *Theatrum Orbis Terrarum*. This work was the first atlas of maps to enjoy wide distribution, and was available in several languages by the year 1612. The third relevant achievement of the time was Lucas Janszoon Waghenaer's *De Spieghel der Zeevaert*, the first dated publication of which was in 1584–85. This was a collection of charts and sailing directions of the European coastlines, bound in one volume. As the Dutch expanded their seaborne empire, it proved to be the forerunner of many fine Dutch sea-atlases, and the Dutch dominated the chart-making industry over the next hundred years. Notable amongst those who flourished in this period were the Amsterdam-based family firms of Blaeu and van Keulen.

Late in the seventeenth century, other nations attempted to challenge the Dutch supremacy in chart-making, notably the British and especially the French. The French founded their official hydrographic office in Paris in 1720, called the Depôt des Cartes et Plans de la Marine. From 1741 to 1772, the head of this department was Jacques Nicolas Bellin. His chart output was prolific and he was responsible for three important marine atlases.

The 1700s saw major advances in Britain's contribution to hydrography. Detailed charts appeared of Britain's own coastline. Then the east coastline of America from Nova Scotia to the Gulf of Mexico was surveyed, while successful charting expeditions were undertaken by Captain James Cook in the South Pacific between 1768 and 1780, and by George Vancouver in Australia, New Zealand and on the Pacific coasts of north-west America from 1791 to 1794.

In 1795, the British Admiralty formed a Hydrographic Office to issue charts to the fleet. By the late nineteenth century, this was able to provide up-to-date charts covering most of the *(cont. p. 79)*

**Printed chart of the English Channel from Dodman Point to Torbay, by Robert Adams, 1590**
This is one of eleven charts produced by Adams to celebrate the defeat of the Spanish Armada in 1588. Ten of them record in detail the series of English Channel engagements between the two rival fleets, from the first sighting of the Armada off the Isles of Scilly to its final defeat off Gravelines. An extra chart of the British Isles shows the track of the Spanish ships through the Channel and around the north coast of Scotland on their homeward-bound journey. Here, English vessels can be seen attacking the Spanish defensive crescent formation off Plymouth, and pursuing them up the Channel.
*G223:2/30 (D3293)*

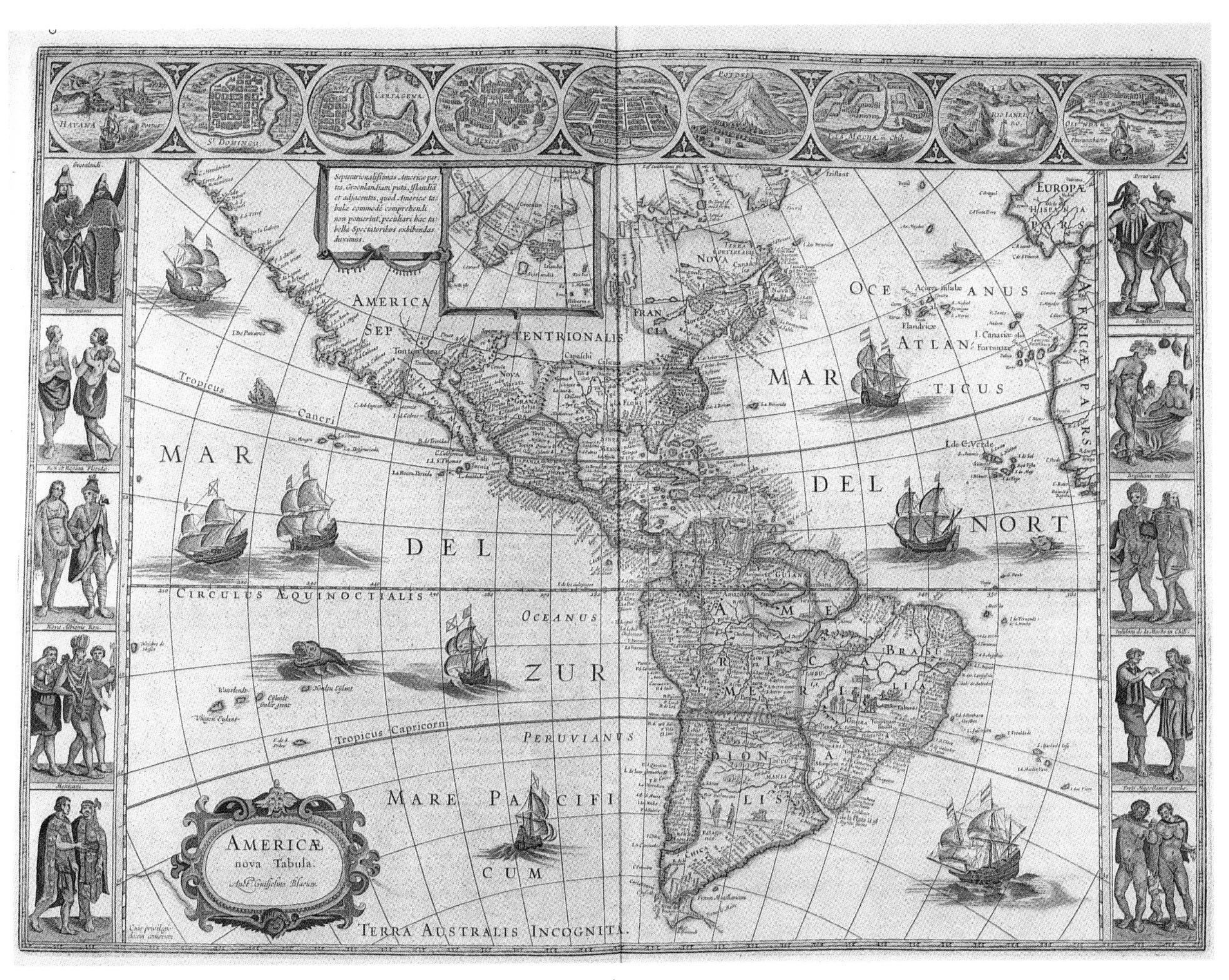


**Printed map of America, by Joan Blaeu, 1662-65**
The Blaeu family of Amsterdam were prominent Dutch cartographers for much of the 17th century. The founder of the business, in 1596, was Willem Janszoon Blaeu, whose first sea-atlas was published in 1608, and soon replaced Waghenaer's. Blaeu followed this success with well known land atlases in 1630 and 1635. On his death in 1638 he was succeeded by his son Joan, who improved and enlarged his father's work into the magnificent twelve-volume *Atlas Maior* of 1662, published in five different languages. The map shown here comes from the *Atlas Maior*. It includes portraits of native Americans and important cities of the New World, including Cartagena, Havana, Rio de Janeiro, and Santo Domingo.
*D5254/11 [D9256]*

**Printed chart of the Gulf of Mexico, by Sir Robert Dudley, 1661**
This chart comes from Dudley's *Dell'Arcano Del Mare*, first translated into English in 1646–47. With it, Dudley's achievement was threefold. His was the first sea-atlas produced by an Englishman, the first to cover the whole known world, and, most significantly, the first in which all the charts were drawn on the Mercator projection. The work also contained information on naval architecture and navigation. An illegitimate son of Queen Elizabeth I's favourite, the Earl of Leicester, Dudley led a voyage of exploration to the West Indies in 1594–95. A knighthood soon followed and, in 1606, after losing favour at court, Dudley went into exile in Florence, where he compiled and published his atlas. This chart comes from the second edition which appeared twelve years after his death.
*D8186 [C6637]*

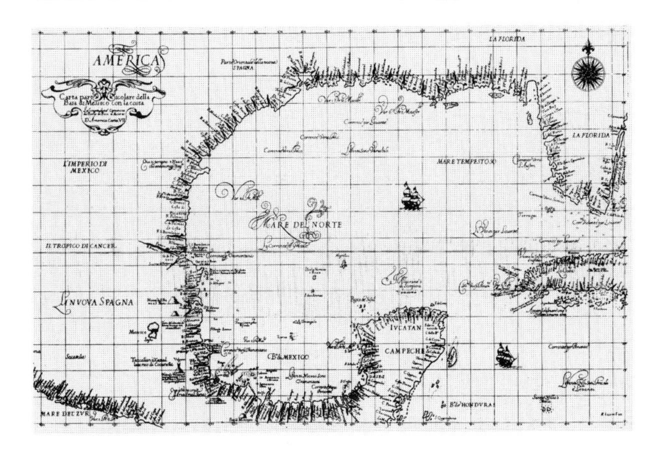

**Engraved chart of the East Indies, by Pieter Goos of Amsterdam, about 1660–68**

Pieter Goos was a well known Dutch chart-maker, engraver and publisher. This portulan was printed on vellum in the mid 1660s. It shows in detail the extent of the area over which the Dutch East India Company enjoyed a virtual trading monopoly for many years, following its foundation in 1602. The eastern headquarters were situated at Batavia (modern Djakarta), and other bases were located in India, Japan, Persia and the Cape of Good Hope. Bankruptcy finally caused the dissolution of the company in 1799. Pieter Goos also produced a series of fine sea-atlases between 1650 and 1667.
*G.250:1/2 [A3968]*

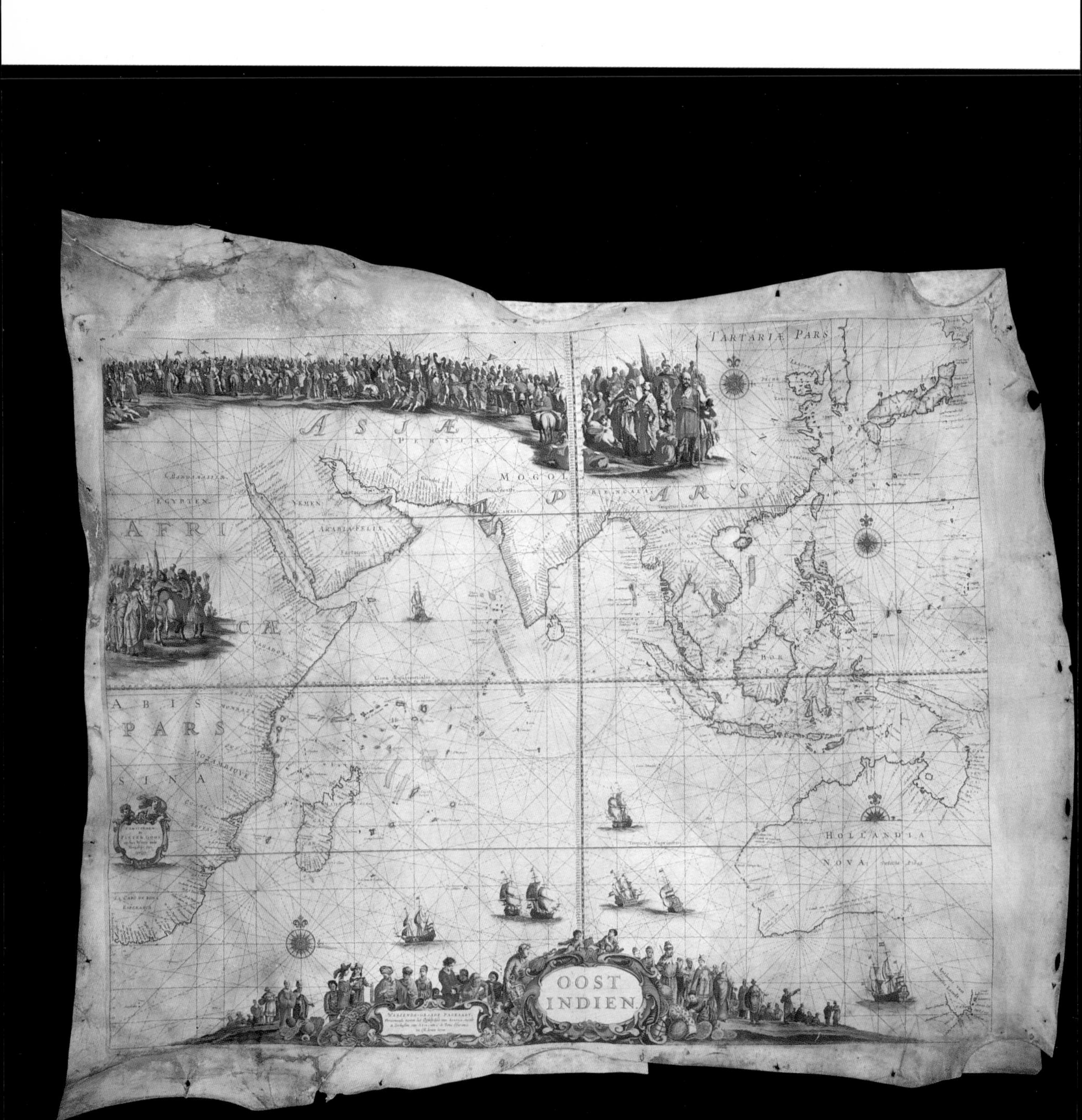

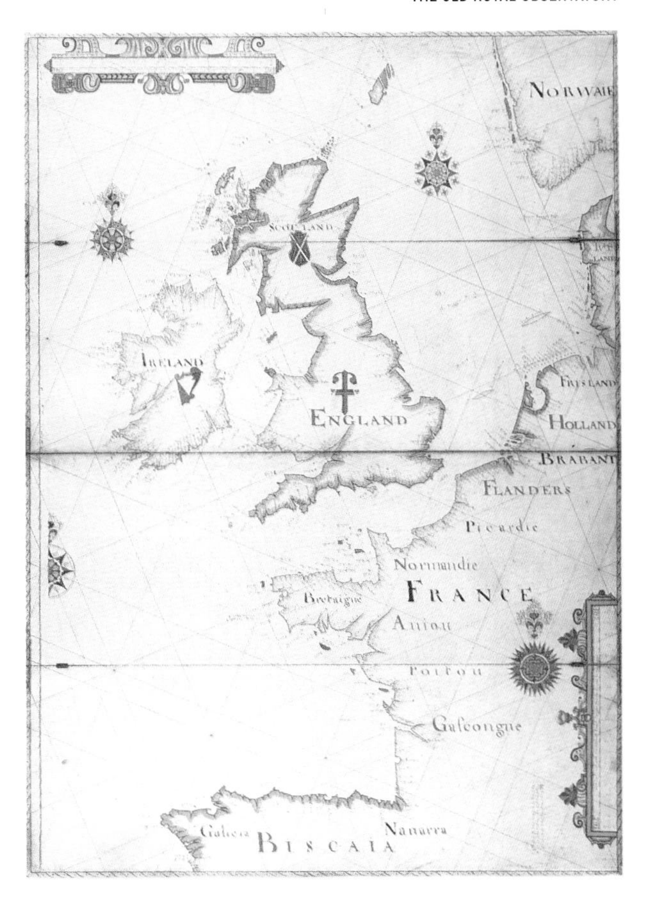


**Manuscript chart, Norway to Cape Finisterre, by Nicholas Comberford of London, 1666**
This chart, drawn on vellum and attached to four hinged oak boards, is a type of portulan generally known as a 'plat'. It was designed to be folded shut when not in use, to protect the chart surface and for easy storage on board ship. The term 'plat' is a variation of the word 'plot' – that is, it is specifically for 'plotting' a course. Comberford was one of the celebrated 'Thames School' of English chart-makers who worked and traded at Ratcliffe, Wapping, on the north bank of the River Thames. Other notable members of this circle were John Burston, Joel Gascoyne and Andrew Welch.
*G.215:1/3 (8173)*

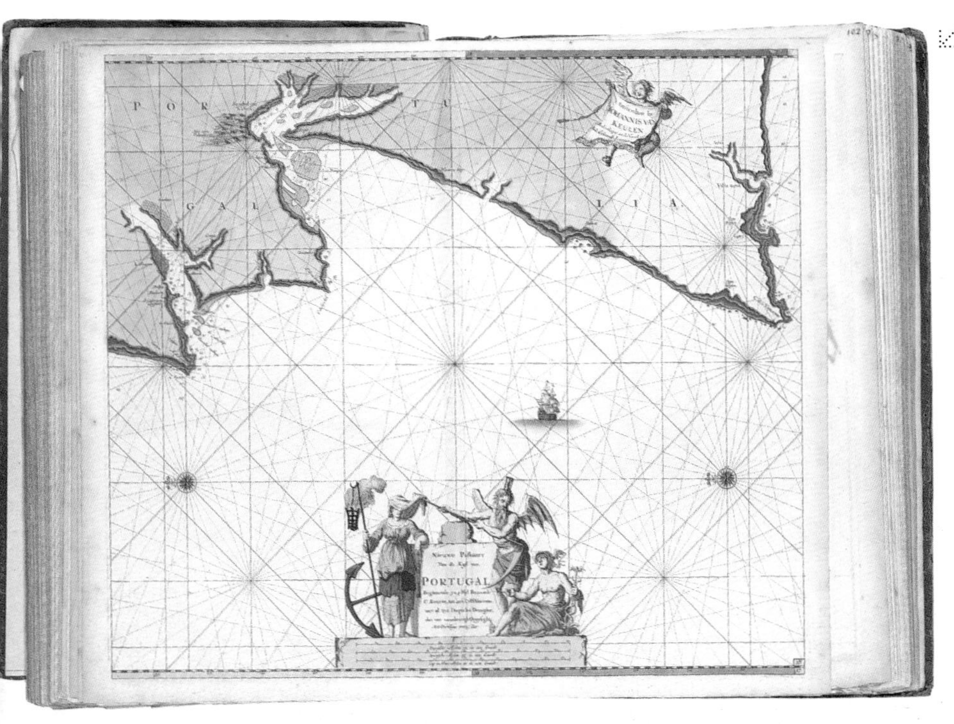

**Printed chart of the coast of Portugal, from Cape Roca to Cape St Vincent, by Johannes van Keulen of Amsterdam, 1680**
The van Keulen family led the Dutch chart-making industry in the 17th and 18th centuries. The business was started by Johannes van Keulen, who first produced the *Zee Atlas* in 1680. He retired in 1704 when control of the firm passed to his son Gerard, who continued to improve and publish his father's work. Editions appeared in Dutch, English, French, Italian and Spanish. Recognition of his contribution resulted in his appointment as Hydrographer of the Dutch East India Company in 1714, a position held to his death in 1727. His son, another Johannes, and grandson, Gerard Hulst, carried on the family tradition. The attractive chart shown here includes a highly decorative cartouche, typical of all van Keulen charts.
*D8037 [D9255]*

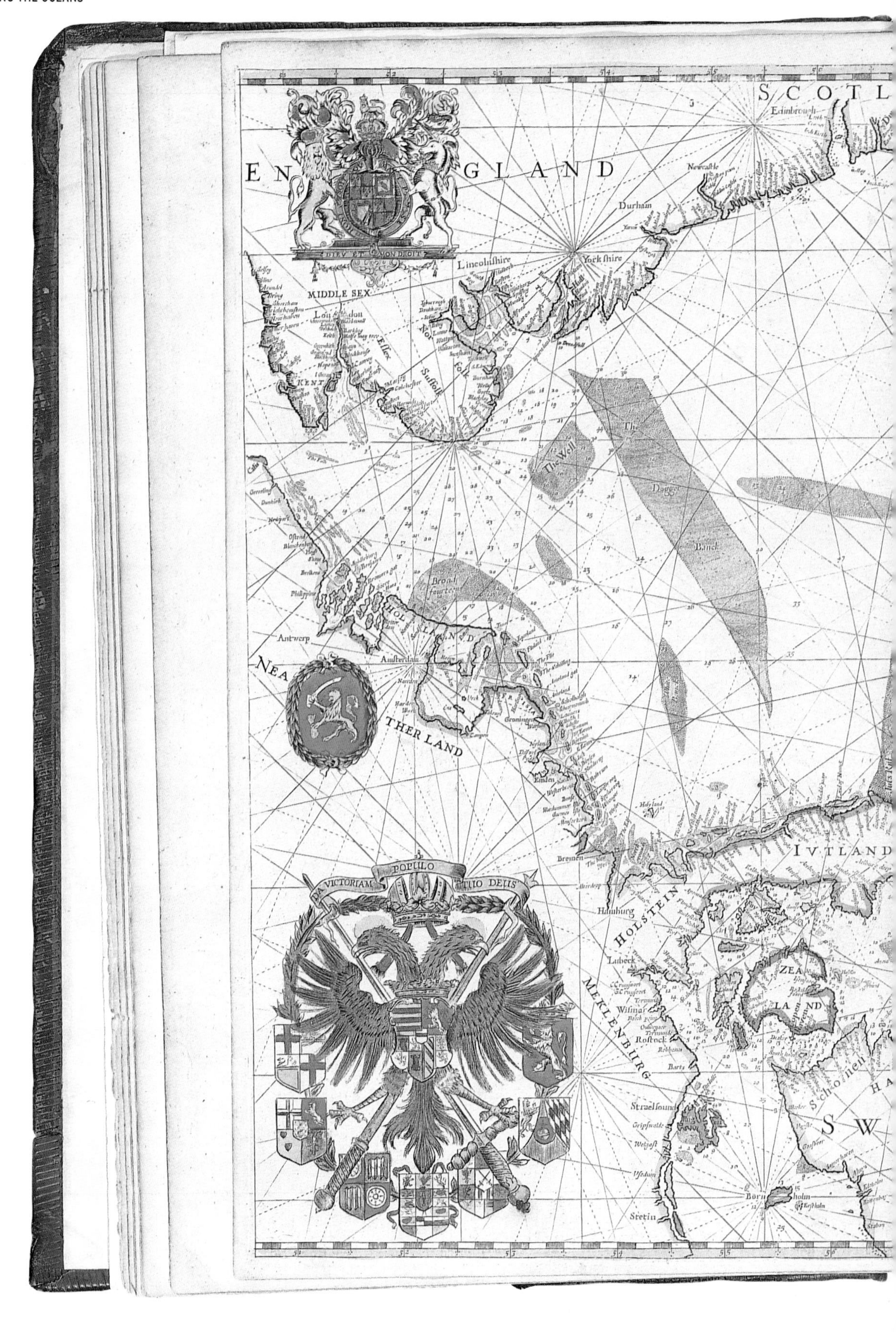
SCOTL
ENGLAND
Edinbrough
Newcastle
Durham
Yorkshire
Lincolnshire
MIDDLE SEX
London
Essex
Suffolk
Norfolk
KENT
The Well
The Dogger Bank
Broad fourteen
HOLLAND
Antwerp
Amsterdam
NEATHERLAND
Groningen
Emden
Bremen
Hamburg
HOLSTEIN
Lubeck
MEKLENBURG
Wismar
Rostock
Straelsound
Stetin
Bornholm
IVTLAND
ZEALAND
Schonen
SW
POPULO

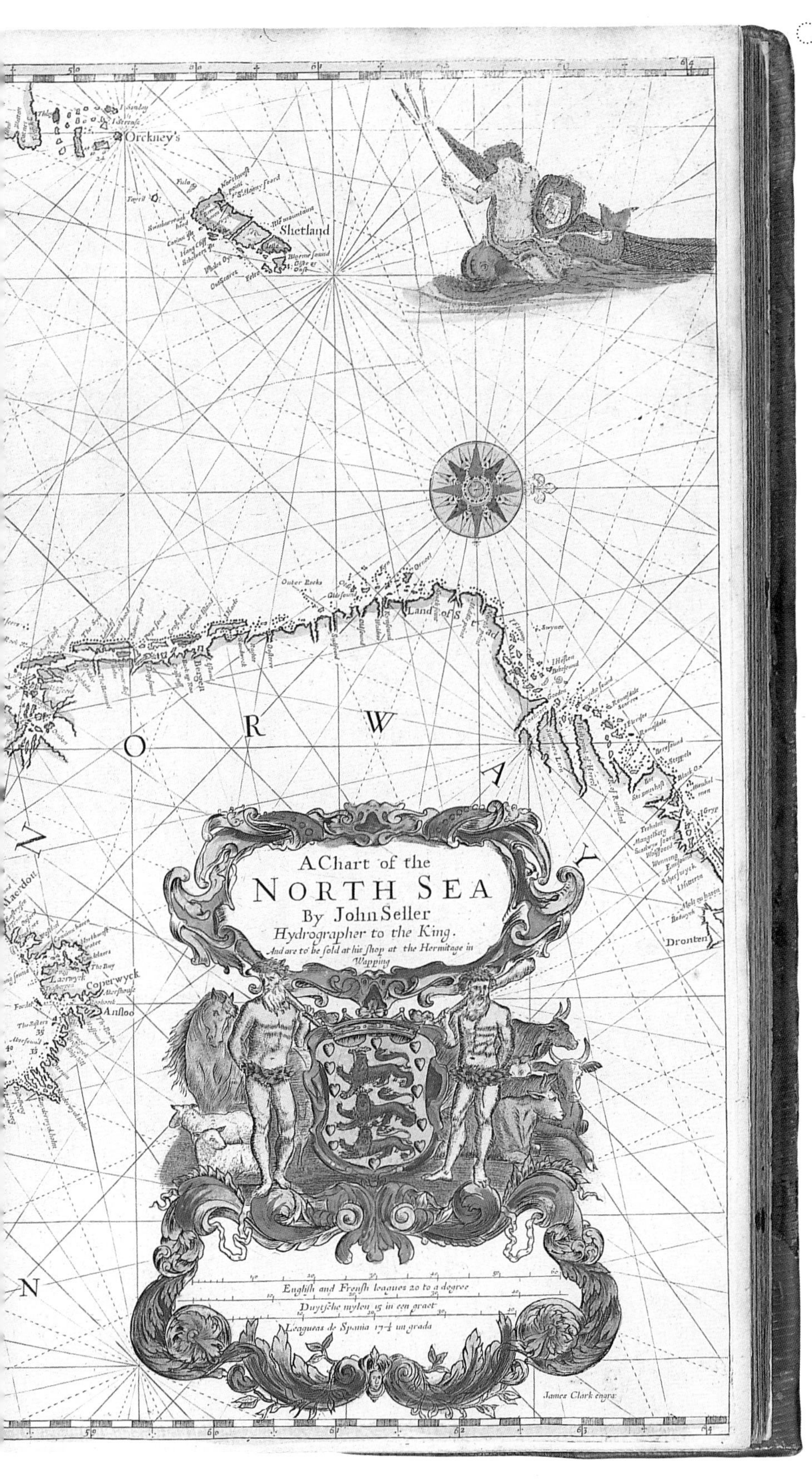


**Printed chart of the North Sea, by John Seller, 1671–72**

The first serious attempt to compete with the Dutch in the marketing of sea-atlases was made by the enterprising London map-maker and publisher John Seller. The first two parts of his *The English Pilot* were first published in 1671–72, and new and updated versions were regularly distributed. The book was eventually available in five parts, covering most of the world, but very little in it was original. A large proportion of the charts were either reprinted or copied from old Dutch plates or surveys. Despite this, *The English Pilot* survived long after Seller's death in 1697, continuing to be available up to 1803. Seller was also responsible for the *Atlas Maritimus*, 1675, *Atlas Minimus*, 1679, and *Hydrographia Universalis*, 1690.
*E6857 [D9257]*

## The winds and waves are always on the side of the ablest navigators.

EDWARD GIBBON, *DECLINE AND FALL OF THE ROMAN EMPIRE*, 1776–88

**Manuscript chart of Acapulco, by William Hack, 1685**
This chart has genuine 'buccaneer' connections and is taken from the 1685 atlas titled *A Waggoner of the South Sea*. The buccaneers were a group of European settlers in the West Indies, who from peaceful beginnings developed into a military alliance that carried out privateering raids against the Spanish colonies in the area during the 17th century. They established a powerful base at Port Royal in Jamaica. Among them was Bartholomew Sharpe, who captured a Spanish ship called the *Rosario* off the coast of South America in 1681. On board, he discovered a *derrotero* or atlas of the South Seas, from which this chart is copied. Sharpe arranged for it to be translated into English and a copy by Hack (one of several he made) presented to King Charles II.
*P.33 [C4563-2]*

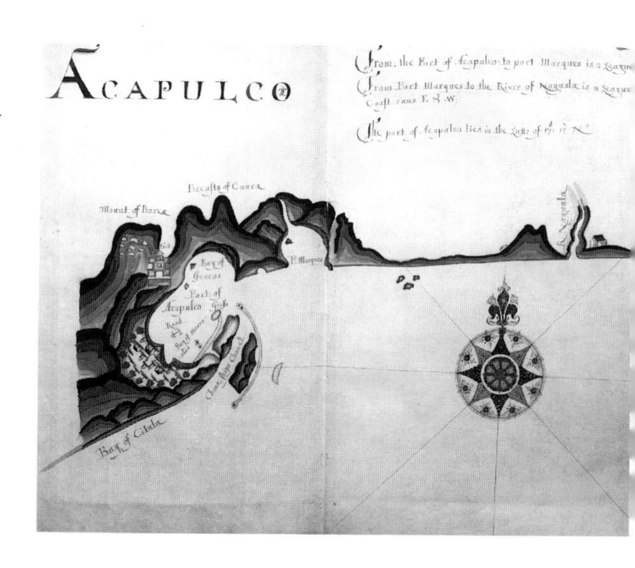

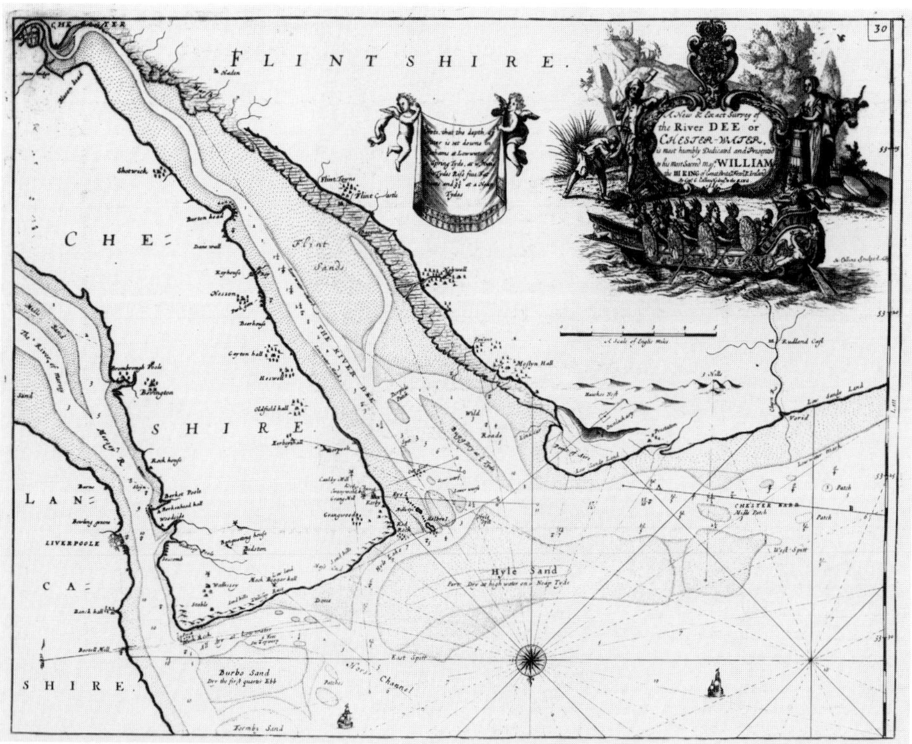

**Printed chart of the River Dee by Greenvile Collins, 1695**
In 1681 Collins was appointed by the British Admiralty to carry out a complete marine survey of Great Britain. It took seven years to complete, but by 1688 Collins had prepared 120 plans of harbours, ports and coastlines, 47 of which were eventually engraved and bound in *Great Britain's Coasting Pilot*, first published in 1693. It was the first sea-atlas in English to cover the British coasts completely. Although criticized as inaccurate by Samuel Pepys, the atlas proved popular with mariners and continued to be available up to 1792. The cartouches on Collins's charts were highly ornate and often dedicated to well known admirals of the period, including Rooke, Russell, and Shovell. This example is dedicated to King William III.
*D8205 [A5314]*

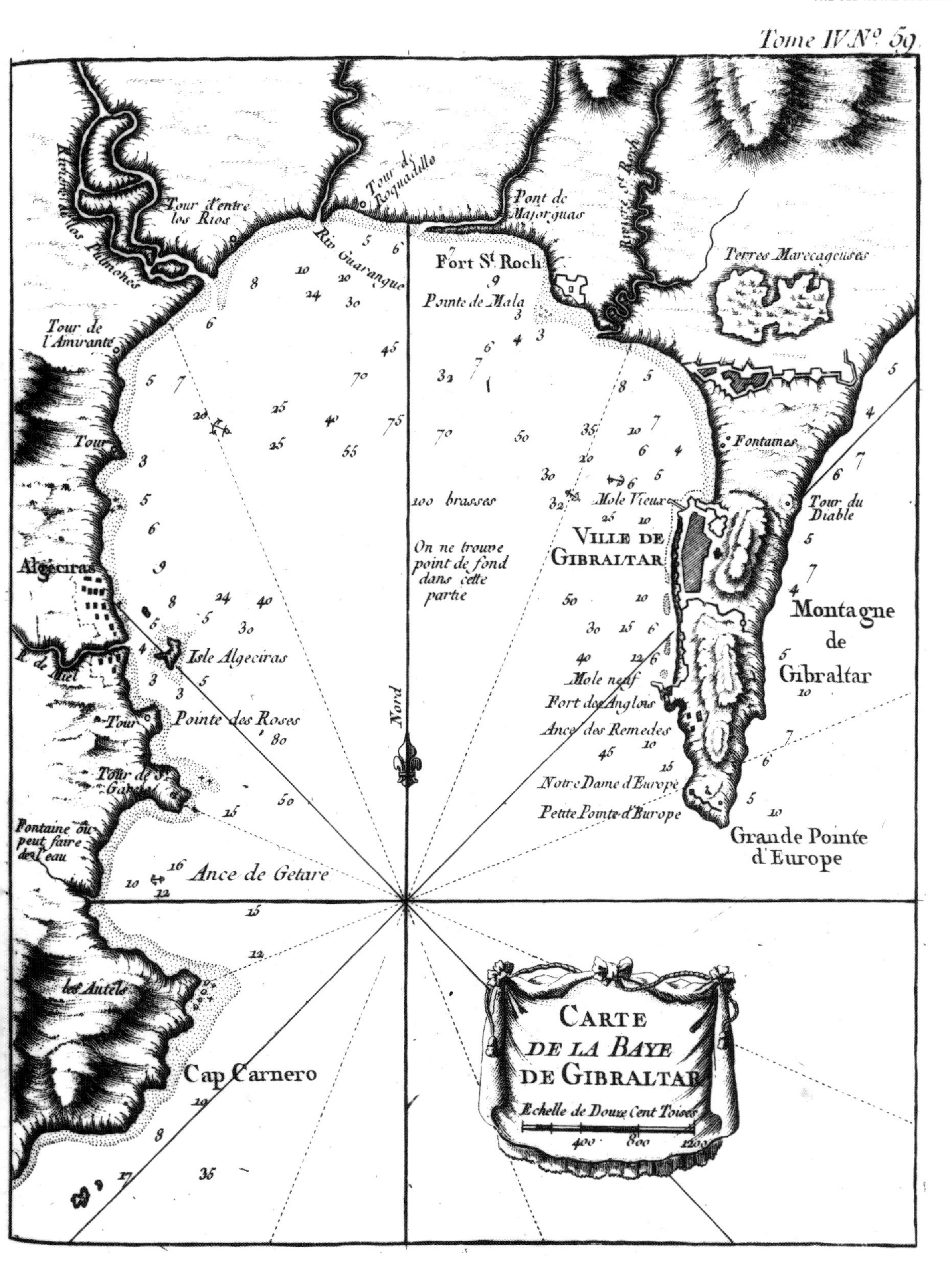


**Printed chart of the Bay of Gibraltar by Jacques Nicolas Bellin, 1764**
The French Hydrographic Office, Le Depôt des Cartes et Plans de la Marine, was founded in Paris in 1720. From 1721, one of the most prolific and important French chart-makers was employed there – Jacques Nicolas Bellin, who from 1741 until his death in 1772 served as the Ingénieur Hydrographique de la Marine, the director in charge of the department. This chart is from Bellin's atlas *Le Petit Neptune François*, first published in 1764. Bellin was also responsible for a new edition of *Le Neptune François* in 1753. This was an updated survey of the coast of France which first appeared in 1693 under Alexis Hubert Jaillot.
*D8194/4 [B5744]*

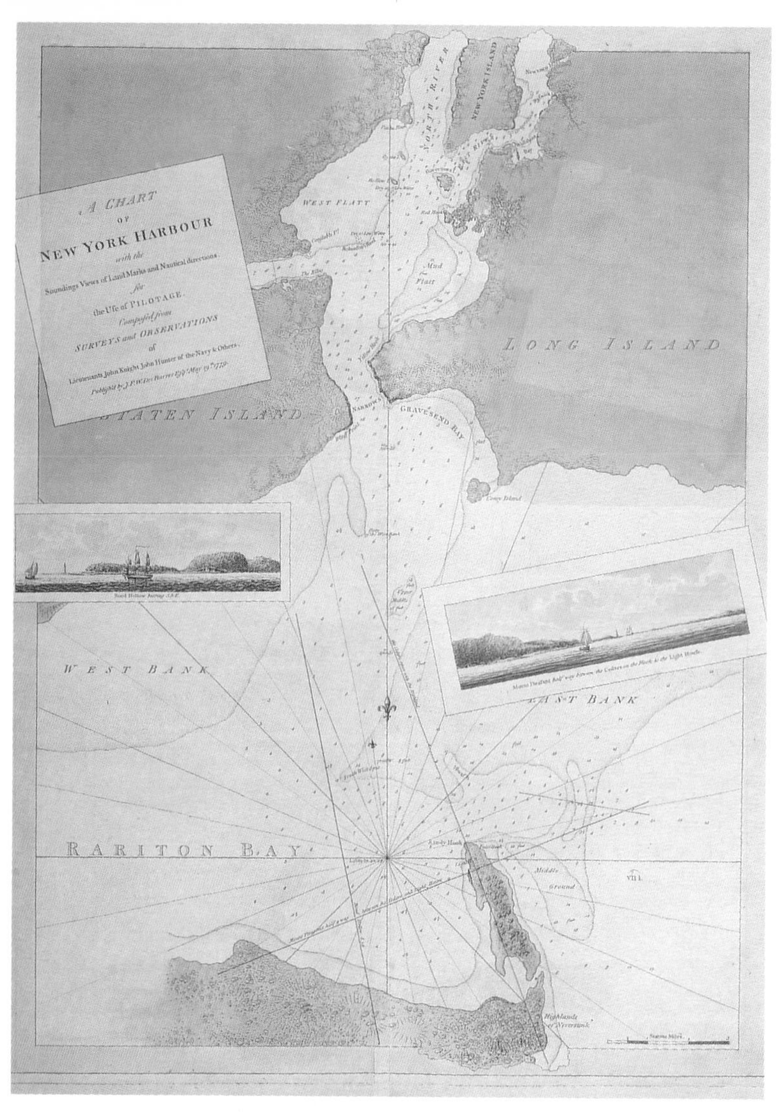


**Printed chart of New York Harbour, by Joseph Frederick Wallet Des Barres, 1779**
This is one of many fine surveys to be found in the *Atlantic Neptune*, a major work compiled by Des Barres, a Swiss-born military engineer in the British Army. Des Barres served in America during the Seven Years War, when he worked with James Cook on a survey of the St Lawrence River. His major achievement was to survey the coastline of Nova Scotia, 1763–73. At the same time, the remainder of the east coast of America, from the Gulf and River of St Lawrence to the Gulf of Mexico, was charted by other officers such as Cook, Hunter and Lane. The results were published in 1784 in the *Atlantic Neptune*, which contained charts, sailing directions and attractive views.
*G.246:2/56 [B5314]*

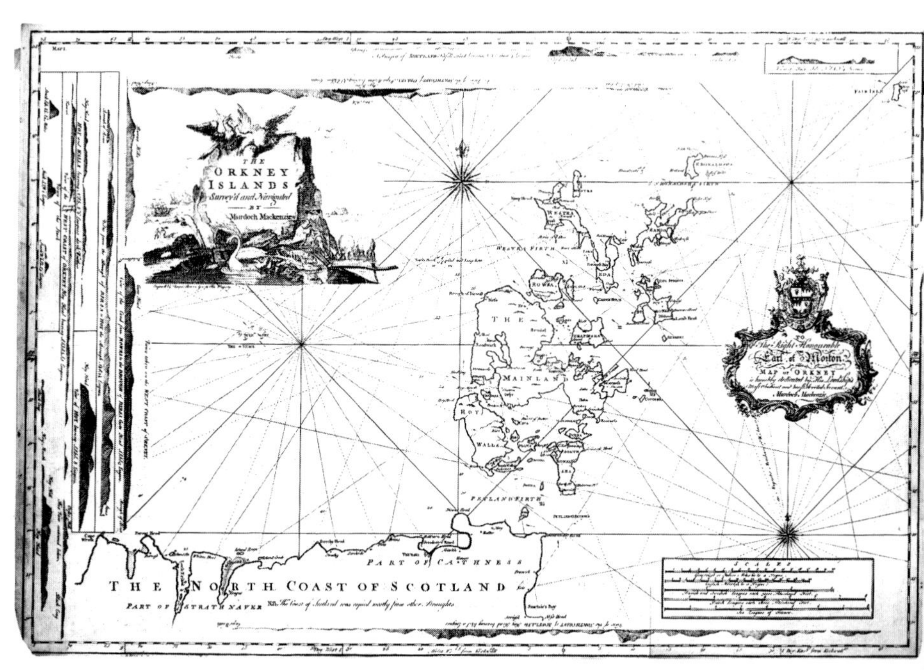


**Printed chart of the Orkney Islands by Murdoch Mackenzie the Elder, 1776**
For several years from 1742, Murdoch Mackenzie carried out a hydrographic survey of the Orkney and Shetland Islands on behalf of the British Admiralty and East India Company. The results were first published in 1750 under the title *Orcades*. This illustration of the Orkneys is from an edition dated 1776. Further charting work on Ireland and the west coasts of Scotland and Wales appeared in 1776, as *A Maritime Survey of Ireland and the West of Great Britain*. Mackenzie was the first surveyor in Britain to use the system of a rigid triangulation and measured baseline. His reference book on the subject, *A Treatise on Maritime Surveying*, was released in 1774.
*D8497 [D8478-C]*

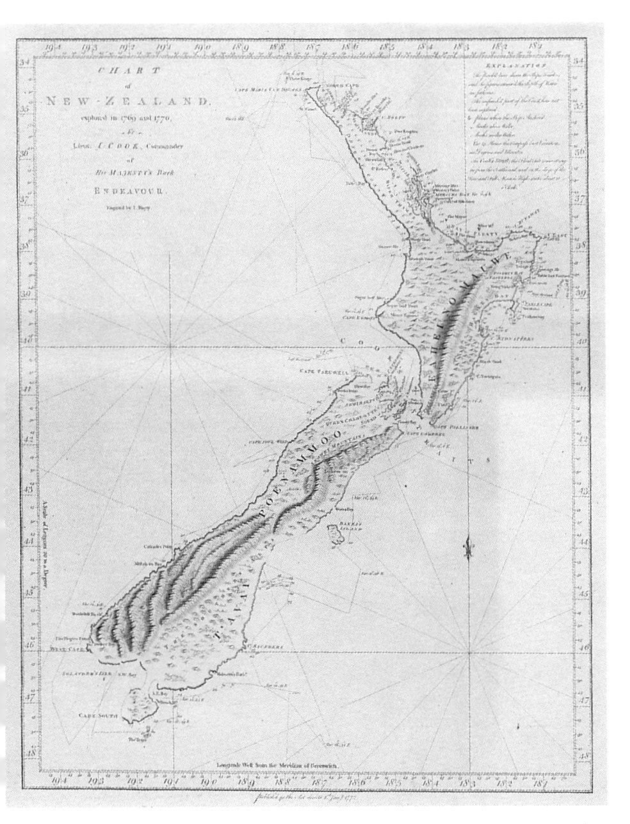


**Printed chart of New Zealand by Lieutenant James Cook, 1772**
Captain James Cook, the most famous of British maritime explorers, joined the Royal Navy in 1755. From 1759, he served as a nautical surveyor in North America during the Seven Years War, where he remained until 1767. Promoted to lieutenant, Cook was chosen in 1768 by the Royal Society to command the *Endeavour* expedition to the South Pacific to search for the imagined great southern continent. After observing the transit of Venus across the Sun on 3 June 1769 in Tahiti, Cook sailed to New Zealand to carry out the first complete survey of its two islands, and produced the chart shown here. Cook also charted parts of Australia's east coast, which he discovered, before the *Endeavour* returned to England in June 1771.
*G.263:1/2 [D9254]*

Earth's coastlines and were foremost in this field.

The necessity for standardization of charts throughout the world was discussed at the first International Hydrographic Conference, held in London in 1919 and attended by twenty-four nations. This emphasized the need for a uniform system of representation on surveys, particularly with reference to symbols, depths and topography. A permanent international chart bureau was therefore established in Monaco in 1921.

Today, many countries operate their own hydrographic offices. They co-operate in ensuring that the latest information is available on charts. New editions and publications regularly appear and computerized charts are now becoming increasingly common.

The hydrography and cartography collections at the National Maritime Museum contain a large number of manuscript and printed charts, atlases and sailing directions, spanning from the early fifteenth century right up to today. With the navigational and astronomical instruments that were necessary in their use, they represent an essential link in the connection between astronomy, timekeeping and safe and reliable voyaging on the world's oceans.
*Brian Thynne, Curator of Hydrography*

***overleaf:*** **Printed chart of the world, by Henry Roberts, 1785**
Captain Cook led three voyages of exploration to the South Pacific. This map shows the tracks of Cook's ships and the discoveries made during his expeditions. During the first voyage in the *Endeavour*, 1768–71, New Zealand was charted and the east coast of Australia surveyed. During the second voyage in the *Resolution* and the *Adventure*, 1772–75, many South Pacific islands were explored and charted and the existence of a great southern continent was finally disproved. The third and final voyage on the *Resolution* and *Discovery*, 1776–80, failed to locate a northern passage between the Atlantic and Pacific Oceans but discovered Hawaii and the Sandwich Islands, where Cook was killed by the inhabitants of Hawaii in February 1779.
*G201:1/5 [D4761]*

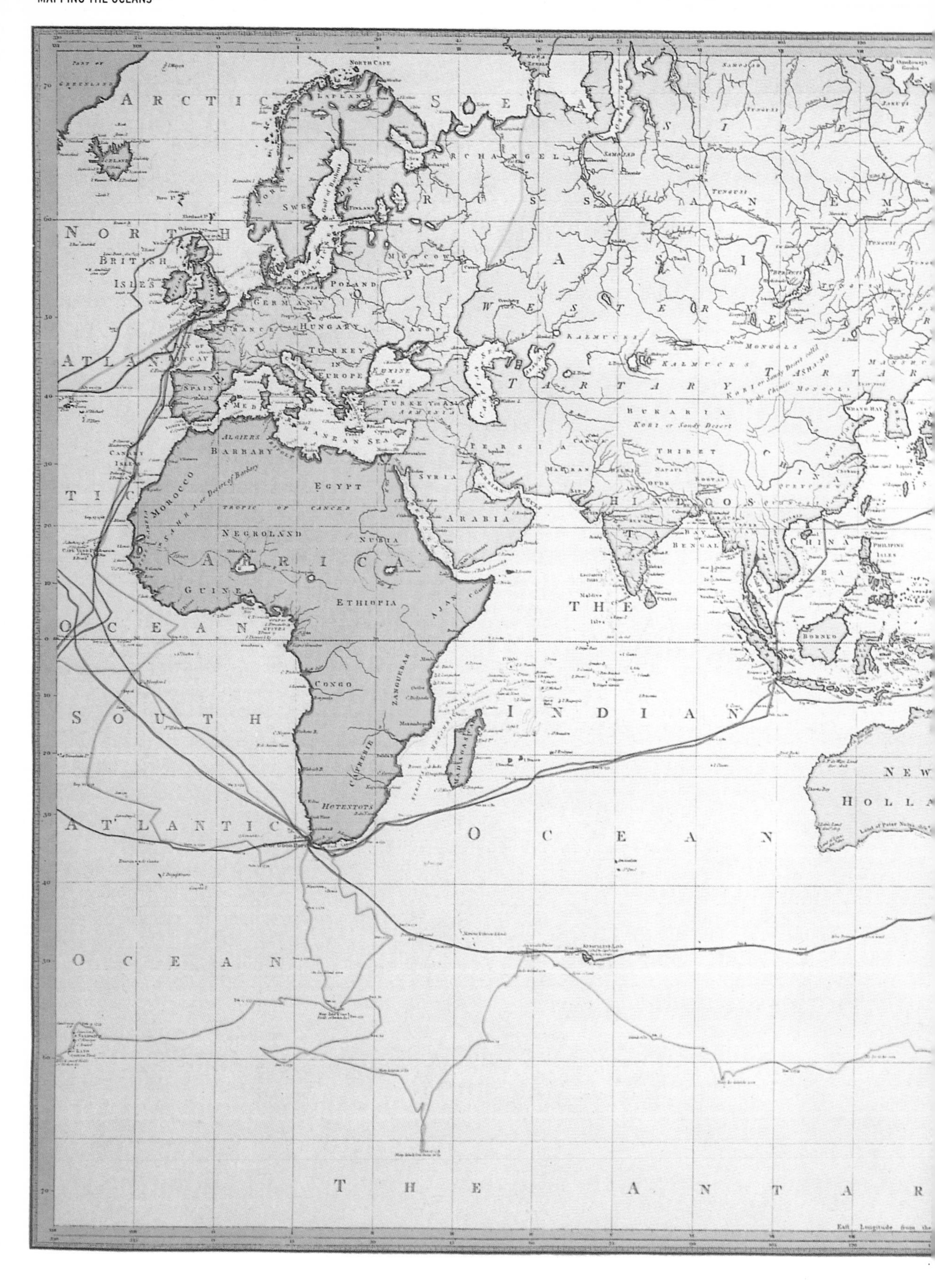
ARCTIC SEA
NORTH CAPE
LAPLAND
ICELAND
NORTH
BRITISH ISLES
SWEDEN
ARCHANGEL
RUSSIAN EMPIRE
MOSCOW
POLAND
GERMANY
HUNGARY
FRANCE
TURKEY IN EUROPE
SPAIN
EUXINE SEA
TURKEY IN ASIA
MEDITERRANEAN SEA
ALGIERS
BARBARY
EGYPT
SYRIA
ARABIA
MOROCCO
TROPIC OF CANCER
NEGROLAND
NUBIA
AFRICA
GUINEA
ETHIOPIA
CONGO
ZANGUEBAR
MADAGASCAR
CAFFRERIA
HOTENTOTS
ATLANTIC
OCEAN
SOUTH
ATLANTIC
OCEAN
WESTERN TARTARY
KALMUCKS
MONGOLS
BUKARIA
KORI or Sandy Desert
PERSIA
THIBET
HINDOSTAN
BENGAL
CHINA
PHILIPPINE ISLES
BORNEO
Maldive Isles
CEYLON
THE INDIAN OCEAN
NEW HOLLAND
THE ANTARCTIC
East Longitude from the

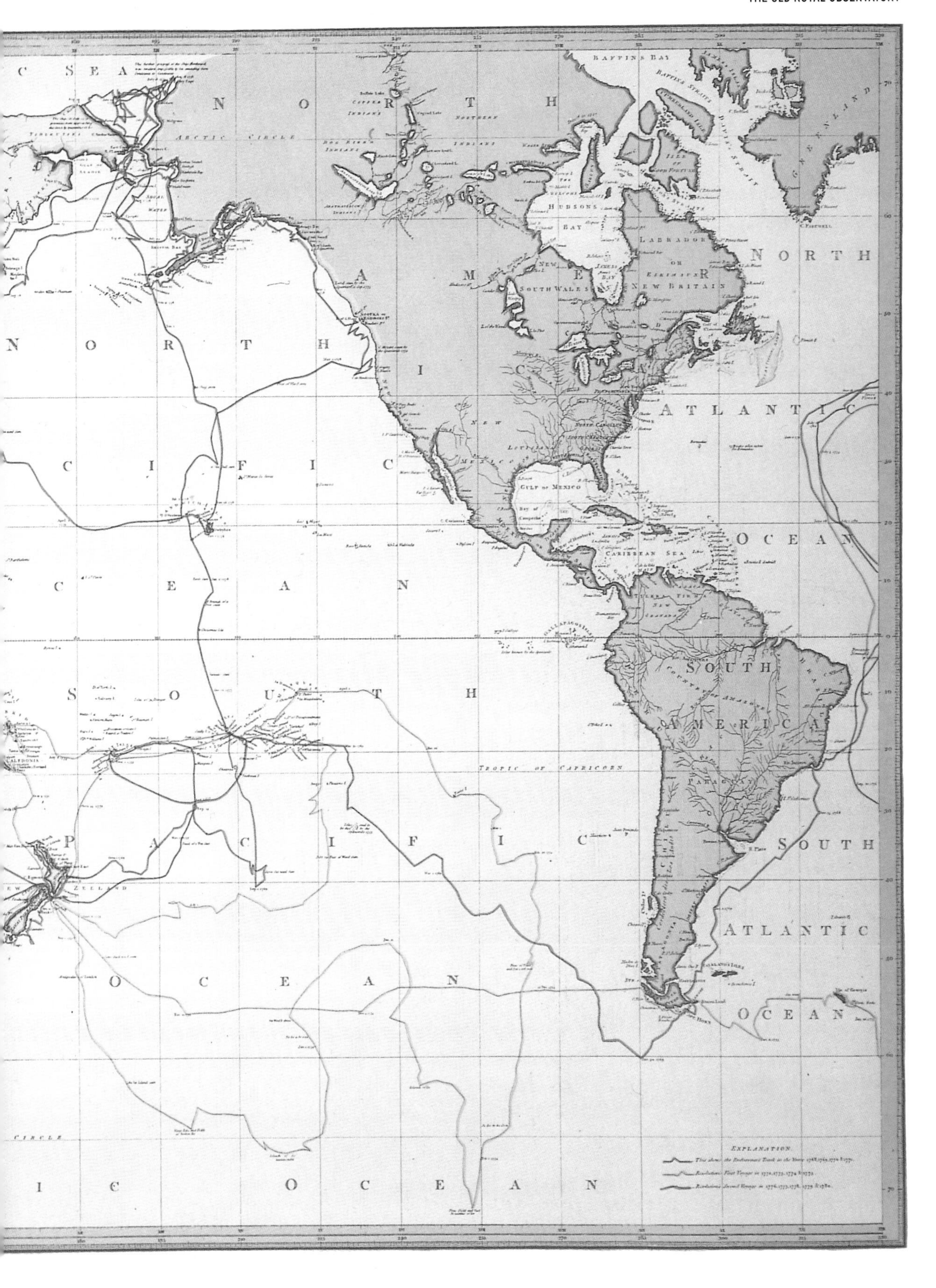
BAFFINS BAY
GREENLAND
NORTH
AMERICA
HUDSONS BAY
LABRADOR OR ESKIMAUX NEW BRITAIN
NEW SOUTH WALES
JAMES BAY
ARCTIC CIRCLE
NORTH ATLANTIC OCEAN
GULF OF MEXICO
CARIBBEAN SEA
SOUTH AMERICA
TROPIC OF CAPRICORN
SOUTH ATLANTIC OCEAN
NEW ZEALAND
NORTH PACIFIC OCEAN
SOUTH PACIFIC OCEAN
EXPLANATION

Let sea-discoverers to new worlds have gone,
Let maps to other, worlds on worlds have showne ...

JOHN DONNE (1572–1631), *THE GOOD-MORROW*

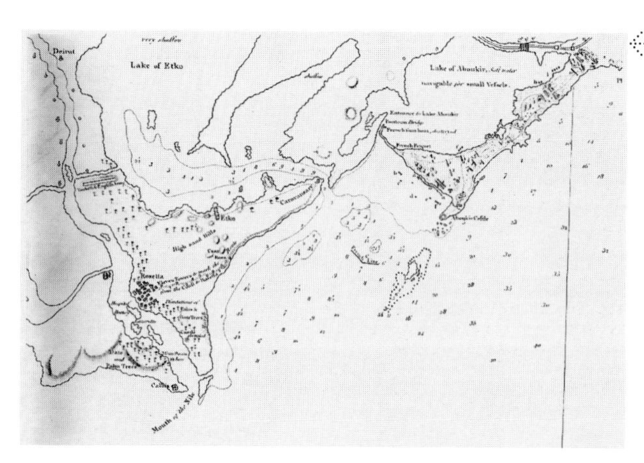


**Printed Admiralty chart of the Coast of Egypt, by Alexander Dalrymple, 1801 (detail)**
Dalrymple was appointed first Hydrographer of the Navy when the British Hydrographic Office was formed in 1795. Through lack of funds he only managed to issue a few charts during his period in office and he was dismissed in 1808. His successors, Captain Thomas Hurd, 1808–23, and later, Rear-Admiral Sir Francis Beaufort, 1829–55, better known for the Beaufort Wind Scale, greatly improved the department and expanded the surveying activities of British ships in home and foreign waters. This detail, from what is probably Dalrymple's first published chart as Hydrographer shows Aboukir Bay, where Nelson defeated the French at the Battle of the Nile, 1 August 1798.
*G.235:14/1 [A8581]*

**Printed chart of Terra Australis, from Mount Dromedary to Cape Hawke, by Matthew Flinders, 1814**
The British naval officer and navigator, Matthew Flinders, was a major contributor to the charting of Australia. Between 1795 and 1800, Flinders assisted George Bass to chart the south-east coast of New South Wales. Together they sailed around Van Diemen's Land, establishing that it was an island and not attached to the mainland, as previously assumed. In 1801–03, Flinders commanded the *Investigator* on another expedition to the Pacific. He completed a circumnavigation of Australia and surveyed a large part of the coast. This chart is a good example of his work and includes a plan of Port Jackson (Sydney), the harbour from where Flinders set out and ultimately returned on his voyage around the continent.
*G.262:4/5 [A7985]*

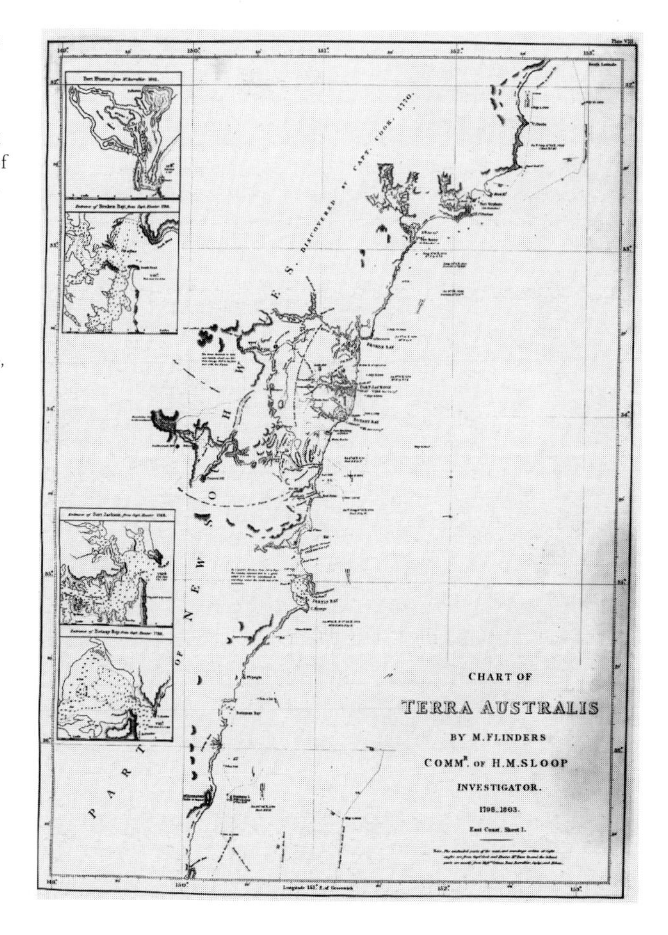

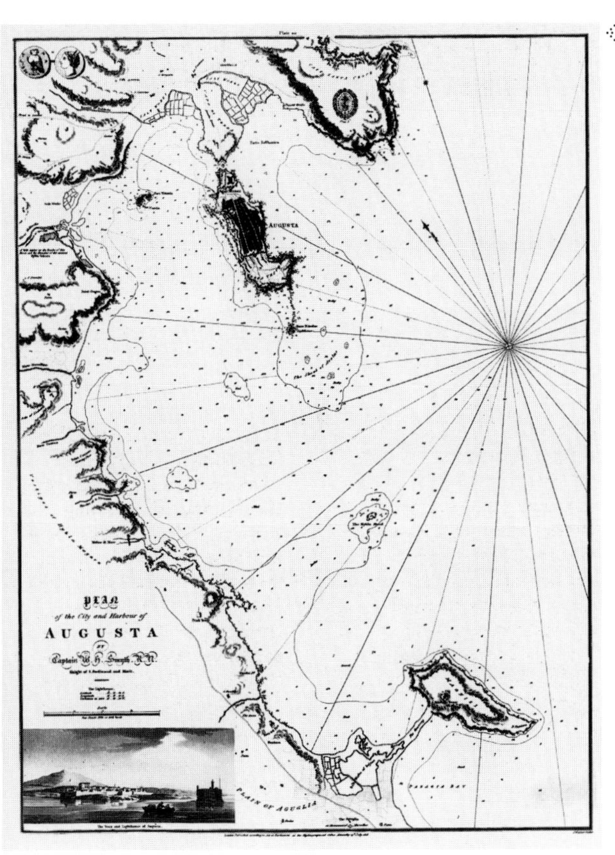


**Printed chart of the City and Harbour of Augusta, by Captain William Henry Smyth, 1823**
Among the most beautiful charts ever published by the British Hydrographic Office were those engraved from the Mediterranean surveys of Captain Smyth, carried out from 1813 to 1823. This example shows the fortified city and harbour of Augusta on the east coast of Sicily, and is taken from the Admiralty publication, *The Hydrography of Sicily, Malta and the Adjacent Islands*. Smyth was an artist of considerable talent, as can be seen from his view of Augusta in the bottom left-hand corner. He was a founder member of the Royal Geographical Society in 1830 and served as its President, 1849–51.
*D8518 [D3144-3]*

**Printed chart of the western coast of North America, from the Gulf of Nicoya to the Gulf of California, by John William Norie, 1846**
Several private companies published sea-charts in the 19th century in direct competition to the British Admiralty. Some firms produced 'bluebacks', named after the colour of the backing paper fixed to the charts. Aimed at the merchant fleet market, bluebacks tended to be larger than the Admiralty surveys and often included a number of insets of port plans, although most of the information was generally obtained from official sources. John William Norie was among the leaders in blueback chart marketing and this is a good example of his work. By 1903, the main companies had merged to form Imray, Laurie, Norie & Wilson, which continues to issue charts today.
*G.278:8/1 (C6641)*

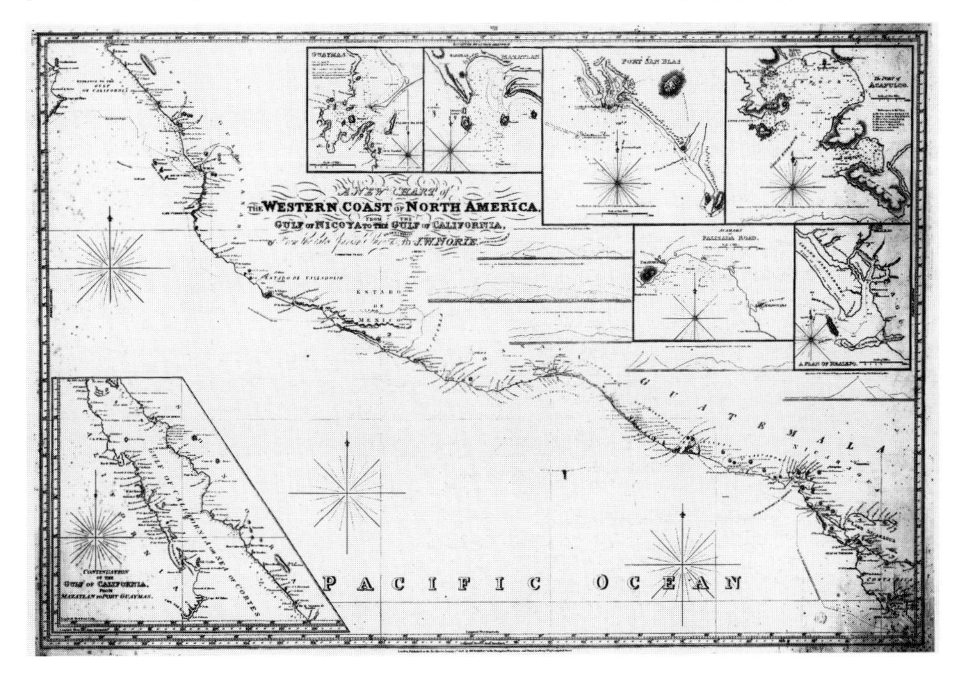

# CHAPTER FIVE

# MARKING THE MERIDIAN

## *The Major Telescopes at the Observatory*

One of the unique aspects of the Observatory collections is the number of telescopes they contain that are important not only to the general history of astronomy but to the history of the Royal Observatory itself. Moreover, several of these telescopes are still on display in or near their original positions in the Meridian Building. The building, in fact, consists of a series of 'rooms' in which astronomical observing took place.

The Royal Observatory differs from many others in the fact that its primary task was positional astronomy – that is, observing and plotting the position of the stars in order to create an accurate and reliable map of the heavens. To do this, the astronomer needs to have one constant reference point from which to measure all of his observations. Given that the Earth rotates,

**John Flamsteed's instruments – a sad tale**
When John Flamsteed died in 1719, his widow removed all the telescopes and clocks from the Observatory, claiming they had been his personal property. Despite a threatened lawsuit by the Office of Ordnance, Mrs Flamsteed stuck by her claim. The result is that none of Flamsteed's astronomical instruments, shown in this engraving by Francis Place, can be traced after 1721.*
*[A5192]*

**Flamsteed's 10-foot mural quadrant, 1676**
The 10-foot (305 cm) mural quadrant was designed by Robert Hooke, made by Thomson of London and had scales hand-divided by Flamsteed himself. The telescope, completed in May 1676, was soon abandoned as its complicated sighting mechanism proved rather dangerous to use. In a letter of July 1678, Flamsteed complains: 'I tore my hands by it and had like to have deprived Cuthbert [his assistant] of his fingers'. It then disappeared from the records and is known to us only through this engraving made by Francis Place in about 1676.*
*[A7121-J]*

**Flamsteed's 7-foot equatorial telescope, 1676**
Flamsteed largely designed his 7-foot (213 cm) equatorial telescope himself. The framework was made by Edward Sylvester of the Tower of London and the wheelwork and indices by the well known clockmaker Thomas Tompion. But the instrument's downfall was its usefulness. Between 1676 and 1698, over 20,000 observations caused its gears and indices to become very worn and inaccurate. From an engraving by Francis Place, about 1676.*
*[A5072]*

We have resolved to build a small Observatory within our park at Greenwich upon the highest ground ... with Lodging room for Our Astronomical Observator and Assistant ...

KING CHARLES II, 22 JUNE 1675
(WARRANT TO BUILD THE ROYAL OBSERVATORY)

**Flamsteed's 7-foot mural arc, 1689**
The appearance of this telescope is preserved in the ceiling decoration of the Painted Hall of the Royal Naval College, Greenwich. In Sir James Thornhill's painting, Flamsteed and his assistant, Thomas Weston, are shown standing beside the mural arc. The paper draped over the balustrade carries a diagram of a total eclipse of the Sun which Flamsteed had predicted for 22 April 1715.
*Courtesy Royal Naval College*

the only reliable reference point is its north-south axis, extended through the sky. This can easily be established by setting the telescope so that it pivots only in one plane, along an arc aligned due north and south. Both on land and in the sky, this north-south axis is known as a meridian. The Meridian Building forms the heart of the Observatory and most of its earliest telescopes are mounted so that they swing only north and south, each along its own meridian.

Today, many of the telescopes on display may appear rather strange or quaint in their form, construction and mounting. During the whole period when the Observatory functioned as an active scientific institution, however, it remained at the cutting edge of technological innovation and development. At different periods during its history the demands that astronomers made of their instruments changed. For example, during the earliest years of the Observatory, the main requirement for a telescope was stability. Telescopes were mounted directly on the Observatory wall so as to ensure minimum movement or vibration. Another feature which underwent study and experimentation was the form of the clamps that held the telescope accurately in its north-south swing. Once these requirements were satisfied, precision in the marking of measuring scales became the focus of attention. Later again, astronomers and scientific-instrument makers turned their attention towards improving the quality of the lenses and optics of the telescope. In order to appreciate fully the story of the Observatory's historic telescopes, it is important to understand the very basic nature of the numerous challenges which faced the Greenwich astronomers in securing an accurate picture of the night sky.

The earliest instruments, belonging to John Flamsteed, the first Astronomer Royal, have all disappeared. They included Flamsteed's seven-foot equatorial sextant, which had a complex mechanism

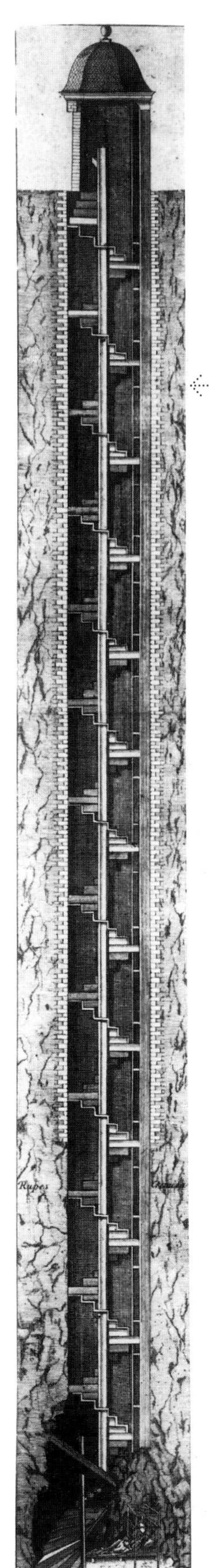


**Flamsteed's well telescope, 1676**
In the garden behind the Meridian Building, a circle of bricks marks the spot where Flamsteed sunk his well telescope. It is easy to forget how basic telescope technology was in the later 17th century. The structure of Flamsteed's well telescope demonstrates some of the problems. A very long tube provides a longer focal length and the possibility of a better image: Flamsteed planned a telescope 90 feet (27.5 m) long. Unfortunately, a very long tube is inherently unsteady and it seems likely that the well telescope was abandoned because the tube was too 'wobbly' to project a clear image. From an engraving by Francis Place, about 1676.*
*[A5192]*

*The engravings marked * on this and the previous two pages are reproduced by permission of the Syndics of Cambridge University Library and the Director of the Royal Observatories.*

**Halley's 8-foot iron mural quadrant and wall, 1725**
Both Halley's and Bradley's 8-foot (244 cm) mural quadrants are mounted on a wall of nine massive stone blocks set into the bedrock of Greenwich Hill. Halley, who had made a name for himself studying the less well known stars of the southern celestial hemisphere, originally set his quadrant on the east side of the wall, roughly in line with Flamsteed's first Greenwich meridian and facing south. The design of Halley's quadrant provides a simple, strong and accurate instrument. Above the wall, the visitor can see remnants of the two viewing slots that were opened in the roof.
*AST0970 [D5598]*

**Halley's 5-foot transit instrument, 1721**
This 5-foot (153 cm) telescope is the earliest at the Observatory that can definitely be associated with its history. Instruments of this sort were a relatively recent invention and Halley's was possibly the first made in England. Lighter and less expensive than a mural quadrant, they had the disadvantage that they could easily become misaligned. Halley's transit instrument, however, proved useful and remained in service, with modifications, until 1750.
*AST0979 [A2839]*

that required at least three people to participate in each observing session. Flamsteed also had a ten-foot mural quadrant, designed by Robert Hooke, but his best known instrument was the seven-foot mural arc which he used to compile his great star catalogue, the *Historia Coelestis Britannica*. Between 1689 and 1719, Flamsteed made some 28,650 recorded observations with this instrument. Flamsteed's well telescope has also disappeared, but its original position is marked in the south garden of the Observatory.

When Edmond Halley became the second Astronomer Royal in 1720, he entered an Observatory devoid of instruments. The Government had promised him £500 to buy new ones, but it was several years before the money materialized. On his arrival, Halley was also shocked to discover that Flamsteed's original observing room – in the corner of the garden behind Flamsteed House – was subsiding down the hillside to the south. When he finally received his money for equipment, nearly all of it had to be spent to build a new and permanent wall for his mural instruments, with only a little remaining for a new eight-foot iron mural quadrant to observe the southern sky. The matching eight-foot brass mural quadrant intended for making observations of the northern sky was not commissioned until 1750, by the third Astronomer Royal, James Bradley. Halley's quadrant remained in active use until August 1812 and Bradley's until August 1813. Both can still be seen in the Meridian Building mounted on Halley's original stone wall.

In 1750, Bradley received a new telescope from John Bird, an eight-foot transit instrument, for which he built a 'New Observatory' on the eastern side of Halley's Quadrant Room. From the moment it was installed, this telescope became the principal meridian telescope of the Observatory and defined Bradley's Meridian, the new Longitude 0°. Bradley's Meridian

Till past 2 of the clock the sun was kept from being seene by Flying cloudes, but soone after wee got a glimpse of him ...

JOHN FLAMSTEED TO RICHARD TOWNELEY, OCTOBER 1677

was used as the Prime Meridian for the first editions of *The Nautical Almanac* (from 1766) and for the land maps produced by the Ordnance Survey from 1791. In 1816, the sixth Astronomer Royal, John Pond, replaced Bradley's eight-foot transit instrument with a ten-foot one designed by Edward Troughton. Both of these are on display in the Meridian Building.

Between 1792 and 1806, Nevil Maskelyne, the fifth Astronomer Royal, made several attempts to acquire a mural circle. Mural circles are wall-mounted telescopes which have a full circle of rotation, allowing astronomers to do a number of tasks, including zenith observations to study the stars directly overhead. It took him more than six years to secure one, but its success prompted

**Bradley's 8-foot brass mural quadrant, 1750 (detail)**
Bradley's quadrant follows the same design as Halley's, the main difference being the metal used. After twenty years of use, the frame of Halley's iron quadrant had buckled under its own weight and become inaccurate. Bradley made his quadrant from brass, a lighter material, in order to overcome this problem. Bradley's quadrant also has an arc which has been hand-divided and signed by one of the great instrument makers of the day, John Bird, as shown in the picture.
*AST0971 [B8286-6]*

**Troughton's 10-foot transit instrument, 1816**
In July 1816, Edward Troughton's 10-foot transit instrument replaced Bradley's earlier one, and reconfirmed Bradley's meridian as the Prime Meridian for the Observatory until December 1850. The telescope itself was regularly calibrated by taking sightings off a number of distant markers. In 1824, a granite obelisk was erected at Chingford, Essex, some 11 miles to the north. The Bradley Obelisk, as it is known, still stands.
*AST0982 [D7061]*

**Bradley's 12½-foot zenith sector, 1727**
This telescope was constructed by George Graham in 1727 for Bradley's personal use in studying the parallax of the star Gamma Draconis. When he was appointed third Astronomer Royal in 1747, Bradley only agreed to bring this instrument to Greenwich after the Government paid him the princely sum of £45 for it. With it he discovered two major phenomena: the aberration of light and the nutation (wobbling) of the Earth's axis. It was used at Greenwich until 1837.
*AST0992 [D7167]*

the seventh Astronomer Royal, Sir George Airy, to design his own. Airy intended to use his new circle not only for observing, but as the main transit instrument of the Observatory. It was erected in a newly built room, in a position exactly 19 feet (5.79 metres) to the east of Bradley's meridian. The first observations were made on 4 January 1851 and, with them, the Airy Transit Circle became the new co-ordinate for the Prime Meridian (Longitude 0°) of the Observatory and, by extension, for all the British navigational charts and the tables printed in *The Nautical Almanac*.

The Ordnance Survey objected greatly to having the Prime Meridian moved away from Bradley's original line on which all their work to date had been based.

**The Airy Transit Circle, 1850**
Constructing Airy's huge transit circle was a major undertaking. The engineering was carried out by Ransomes & May of Ipswich and Troughton & Sims constructed both the optical parts (including the 8 1/8-inch [206 mm] object lens) and the main body, but the instrument was designed almost wholly by Airy himself. As the transit circle was not wall mounted, repeated use often meant that the telescope fell out of true vertical alignment. To remedy this it was re-aligned (or collimated) weekly. From 1854, a recording apparatus, or chronograph, was introduced to record its observations on a rolling drum of graph paper.
*AST0991 [D7064]*

In 1884, therefore, when Airy's meridian was voted as the Prime Meridian of the World at the International Meridian Conference in Washington DC, the Ordnance Survey announced that, from that moment, Britain would have two official meridians: one which was recognized internationally for astronomy and navigation, and one which served as the basis for all of Britain's land maps. This remains largely the situation today.

The largest telescope at the Observatory is the 28-inch visual refractor, also known as the Great Equatorial Telescope from the fact it is mounted on a so called 'equatorial mounting'. This means that the axis of the support points directly towards the northern celestial pole. The telescope was ordered from Sir Howard Grubb of Dublin in 1885, when it was decided that the Merz 12-inch refractor located in the south-east Equatorial Dome was no longer sufficient. In order to fit the new telescope into the existing building, the covering dome had to be modified from a drum-shape to the distinctive 'onion' design that visitors can see today. The new telescope was first used in 1894 and its 28-inch-diameter (71 cm) object glass was so superb that the telescope became an essential tool for observing double stars (pairs of stars whose orbits are so closely linked that they often look like single stars). Today, the 28-inch refractor remains in full working order, though it now has computer-assisted tracking and a camera that can be added to the eyepiece to allow the image it captures to be seen on a television monitor.
*Kristen Lippincott, Director, Old Royal Observatory*

**Troughton's 6-foot mural circle, 1810**
Commissioned from Edward Troughton, with the optical parts by Peter and John Dollond, this 6-foot (183 cm) mural circle was first used in 1812. Thanks to its scale of 360°, it dispenses with the need for a plumb line in order to find an accurate 0°. At first, it did not appear sturdy or stable enough to function as a reliable transit instrument but, after new clamping was added in 1822, it was so versatile that all the other telescopes paled by comparison. The upper picture on page 91 shows the circle on the far wall.
*AST0973 [B8230]*

**The 28-inch refracting telescope, 1885–93**

Twice in its history, observations with the 28-inch refractor have been disturbed. The first time was during World War I. Then, in 1939, the valuable object glass was sent to a place of safety during World War II. This was just as well, since the Observatory was damaged by bombing and in 1944 the covering of the dome itself was stripped off by a V1 flying bomb. In 1947, the telescope was dismantled and sent to Herstmonceux, leading the departure of the astronomers from Greenwich. It was fully operational there from 1957 to 1970, but was then 'retired' and sent back to Greenwich to mark the Observatory's 300th anniversary in 1975.
*AST0932 [D5614]*

The Earth, that is sufficient
I do not want the constellations any nearer,
I know they are very well where they are
I know they suffice for those who belong to them.

WALT WHITMAN (1819-1892), *SONG OF THE OPEN ROAD*

**The telescopes at Herstmonceux Castle**
When the Royal Greenwich Observatory moved to Herstmonceux Castle in the 1950s, a number of the larger telescopes left Greenwich with it. For example, a 13-inch (33 cm) astrographic refractor made by Grubb of Dublin in 1888 (which had been used to generate information for the famous star-map, the international *Carte du Ciel*) was moved to Herstmonceux in 1958 and set within a 22-foot hemispherical dome. Similarly, a 26-inch (66 cm) photographic refractor, made by Grubb in 1896, was mounted in Dome E at Herstmonceux in 1957. The Yapp 36-inch (91.5 cm) reflector, built in 1932, was used at Greenwich for spectroscopy, or the study of the chemical composition of stars. It was moved to Herstmonceux in 1958.
*[B640]*

## ASTRONOMERS ROYAL, PAST AND PRESENT

| | |
|---|---|
| John Flamsteed | 1675-1719 |
| Edmond Halley | 1720-1742 |
| James Bradley | 1742-1762 |
| Nathaniel Bliss | 1762-1764 |
| Nevil Maskelyne | 1765-1811 |
| John Pond | 1811-1835 |
| Sir George Biddell Airy | 1835-1881 |
| Sir William Christie | 1881-1910 |
| Sir Frank Dyson | 1910-1933 |
| Sir Harold Spencer Jones | 1933-1955 |
| Sir Richard Woolley | 1956-1971 |
| Sir Martin Ryle | 1972-1982 |
| Sir Francis Graham Smith | 1982-1990 |
| Arnold Wolfendale | 1991-1994 |
| Sir Martin Rees | 1995- |

### FURTHER READING


- Jonathan Betts, *John Harrison,* London 1993
- *The Preface to John Flamsteed's* Historia Coelestis Britannica *or 'British Catalogue of the Heavens'* [1725], ed. A. Chapman, trans. Alison Dione Johnson, London 1982
- Eric G. Forbes, A.J. Meadows and Derek Howse, *Greenwich Observatory,* 3 vols., London 1975
- Derek Howse, *Greenwich Time and Longitude,* London 1997
- Nevil Maskelyne, *The Seaman's Astronomer,* Cambridge 1989
- Kristen Lippincott, *A Guide to the Old Royal Observatory: The Story of Time and Space,* London 1997
- Stuart Malin and Carole Stott, *The Greenwich Meridian,* Southampton 1984
- E. Walter Maunder, *The Royal Observatory Greenwich: A Glance at its History and Work,* London 1900
- William Hunter McCrea, *Royal Greenwich Observatory: An Historical Review issued on the occasion of its Tercentenary,* London 1975
- Colin A. Ronan, *Edmond Halley, Genius in Eclipse,* London 1969
- Colin A. Ronan (ed.), *Greenwich Observatory: 300 years of Astronomy,* London 1975